To
my 'pal

Thank-you ~~~~~~
'light' on my darkest
times at the beginning
of my amazing soul-
searching journey towards
light, love & forgiveness.

Take care & god bless
Jacinta

Jacinta is a fifty-eight-year-old single parent with a fifteen-year-old son.

She is the survivor of a family affected by alcoholism, physical, emotional and sexual abuse.

She ran her own training consultancy business for over fifteen years, writing and facilitating interactive, leadership, sales and customer care workshops in the UK and Ireland. She worked closely with the NHS in the implementation of PALS – Patient Advice and Liaison Service.

A sudden diagnosis of Breast Cancer in 2004 presented Jacinta with a unique opportunity to confront and heal the Cancer of her past allowing her true 'godness' to shine as it had never done before. The hidden gifts are magnificent and glorious.

Hidden Gifts

DEDICATION

This book is dedicated to all those children who once were, who need to find their voices to heal.

Jacinta McShane

Hidden Gifts

An abuse survivor's triumph through cancer

AUSTIN MACAULEY

A CIP catalogue record for this title is available from the British Library.

ISBN 978 1 84963 013 9

www.austinmacauley.com

First Published (2010)
Austin & Macauley Publishers Ltd.
25 Canada Square
Canary Wharf
London
E14 5LB

Printed & Bound in Great Britain

ACKNOWLEDGEMENTS

A special thank you to my son Josh,
for your amazing love and courage.

Thank you guiding angels and family of loving friends.
Your spiritual guidance and support
throughout our journey
has been truly 'heaven-sent'.

Josh and I could not have done this without you!

Hidden Gifts

An Abuse Survivor's Triumph through Cancer

'I needed Cancer in my life to heal completely'

From Disease to Complete Healing

Such gratitude
I can never repay
Such humility
I have never experienced
Such power
I never knew I had
Such beauty
I have never seen
Such freedom
I have never known
Such truth
I have never released
Such peace
I have never felt
Such life
I have never cherished

Cancer has given these beautiful gifts
to my son and me
We share them with you
with our love

Contents

1

Explanation of Terms and Names
used in this book

Cinty, Cindy and Jacinta

I was christened Jacinta. In this story, I am known as 'Cinty" by my family, and 'Cindy' in my early working years.

Bazookas

Mammy – a petite, slim, attractive woman had breasts that looked like bazookas. Throughout this story, my mother's breasts are referred to as 'bazookas'.

Dis-ease

I refer to Cancer throughout this book as dis-ease being spiritual unrest as opposed to disease as a pathological condition. Robert Burney – author of *The Dance of Wounded Souls* sums up dis-ease as: 'Not being at ease, at one with Spiritual Self. Not being able to be in balance, in harmony with the universe. All other diseases – physical, emotional, mental – spring out of, are caused by, spiritual dis-ease.'

Cc-ancer

Cancer is spelt with a capital 'C' up to the entry on 27th February '07 in chapter 21 – my salvation. Cancer has power over me up to this point.

Cancer is spelt with a small 'c' from this moment on to the end of this story reflecting my power over cancer.

Godness

Godness is a blessed blend of innate goodness and God within each one of us.

Wholistic

Wholistic care is the nurturing and treatment of the entire person physically, emotionally, spiritually and mentally with the emphasis on the 'whole'.

Homes. The Bank House and Limavady Road

As a family we lived initially in the Bank House and later in Limavady Road in Derry, Northern Ireland.

The Bank House in Shipquay Street (Ages 2 – 15)

The Bank House is situated on the corner of Castle Street and Shipquay Street – the main street in the centre of Derry on a slight incline leading down to the docks by Lough Foyle. Built early in the 1900s, this huge stone edifice is our home and daddy's workplace rolled into one. The Hibernian Bank as it is known, takes up the entire ground floor and part of the basement. This is Daddy's domain, the only place where he is in charge. Rich, mahogany counter with tall, wrought-iron railings separate the staff from the customers who enter from the Shipquay Street entrance. Daddy has his own private office at the far end and a small cubicle next to it where he can serve customers. Four cashiers each have their own cubicle alongside. Old, worn wooden floorboards support this office which is busy five days a week and most evenings when daddy works late.

At the back, a private door opens to our home which has a large marble-tiled hall and separate entrance from Castle Street. Just behind the stairs lies a small, stone-floored area with entrance to the back yard outside and a wooden, latched door to the foreboding coal cellar below. Long winding stairs lead up to our fourteen-roomed home on a further three floors. A spacious landing opens out to five rooms on the first floor: the kitchen where we spend most of our time, eating, watching TV, praying and fighting; the posh drawing room where mammy impresses her friends playing the piano, drinking into the small hours and holding office parties to impress daddy's work colleagues; the large living room, with huge mahogany dining table and matching side-board covered in silverware and cut crystal glasses. Here I often play with my brother and sister. Santa leaves our Christmas presents here, too. Next to it lies the long, unused pantry with rows of mostly empty cupboards where I hide sometimes, and shelves, some containing mammy's ill-fated attempts at making damson jam. Then opposite our kitchen is mammy's and daddy's bedroom with two beds, one double and one single. This is where I make daddy stop loving me.

Our bedrooms are on the second floor. There is a toilet at the top of the stairs next to my pink wall-papered bedroom, which looks out on to the back yard below. Opposite is my brother's and sister's bedroom and past that, the large, plain, greenish bathroom – another hiding place – from mammy's rages. There are two further messy rooms at the far end, which we mainly use as playrooms. Upstairs in the attic are three more spare rooms, one with a loft window out on to the sloping slated roof high above the road. Most rooms are huge with high ceilings and fireplaces. I love this house but I am not happy here.

Limavady Road (Ages 15-19)

Our new home is daddy's retirement home, the first home that he has had actually to buy. No porter here, no busy office downstairs, no business parties, no more outside caterers. Here we are on our own. A Victorian detached house, white stone with black woodwork and a small back garden, situated in a residential area on the main road to Limavady, a town some 17 miles away. Downstairs on the ground floor is a sitting room which we call the 'blue room' and where we spend most of our time; a dining room with our piano, which is our best room and where we spend very little time; kitchen with Aga cooker, kitchen table and small scullery; and a ground floor bathroom. Upstairs are a separate toilet and four bedrooms. Quite a bit smaller than we were used to and a world away from mammy and daddy's comfortable, social lifestyle. This is when daddy gets sick.

2

Introduction: Past and Present

It's impossible to predict how each of us will react until we come face to face with major challenges in our lives. Difficult and often traumatic experiences can offer us wonderful opportunities to dig deep into who we really are and unearth our true 'godness'.

As a single professional mother with a nine-year-old son, my sudden diagnosis of an aggressive form of invasive Breast Cancer in May 2004 at the age of 52 turned our world completely upside down. Reeling from one crisis to another, we struggled to cope as a family, stumbling and staggering along this emotionally and physically challenging path.

Writing this book was not a conscious decision but one borne of my immediate reaction to my Cancer diagnosis. Floundering under the shock, I came home feeling so alone, completely devastated, and immediately started pouring out my thoughts and feelings on to my computer. This was my private place, my soulmate; somewhere I could turn to share my fear, despair, anger and keep a grip on what was happening to me and my son.

This is not a book about magical Cancer cures nor is it about my 'fight' or 'battle' with Cancer. I am not a doctor nor a qualified authority on Cancer but I am an informed cancer patient. Part of my challenging, yet empowering, experience has involved making my difficult way through our beleaguered health service, speaking up honestly about how I feel, challenging opinions, making difficult choices but always making my own decisions. The information about various complementary therapies and treatments in this book are the result of my personal search for the best whol-istic treatments to complement my conventional medical treatment. Comments about unnamed professionals or organisations are in no way personal but designed to reflect the strengths and weaknesses of an overworked, target-driven and pharmaceutically-led system. In fact, my speaking out assertively throughout my treatment belies my utter terror at what is happening to me and, unbeknown at the time, begins a remarkable process of inner healing.

The guts of this story goes back to the early 1950's in Northern Ireland. As a child, my family was a picture of perceived middle-class respectability and success – a glamorous, talented, outgoing, youthful mother and a much older, reserved, intelligent, academic, professional father, with three beautiful children: 'Pillars of the community', so to speak. The reality however was totally different. My childhood as part of this family harboured an intricate, secret web of physical, sexual and emotional abuse.

On the one hand, stripped of any affectation, this is a raw story of the traumatic but enlightening and liberating effect of Cancer upon our family, captured in journal format as it occurs, with my son's experience illustrated in his emotive sketches, observations and comments. On the other, this is a much deeper story, with Cancer acting as a catalyst for my complete spiritual healing, revealed in narrative flashbacks to my troubled childhood which are interspersed throughout the main text. Cancer enabled me to find the courage to confront myself and give birth to a beautiful but suppressed, and deeply ashamed part of myself, bringing amazing hidden gifts into our uncertain world.

I hope that our raw experience will help you find your inner voice, view your traumatic experience for the 'real' message and the amazing hidden, 'healing' gifts that it can bring to each and everyone of us.

3

'Life' Before

Encumbered by deeply masked feelings of inadequacy, insecurity, betrayal, shame and fear, I approached life as if it were a constant threat to me. These underlying feelings and attitudes manifested themselves in a relentless need to prove myself. Hence the working side of my life dominated, as this was where I could feel 'in complete control', leading me into demanding careers in sales and training consultancy. Having begun my sales career in my mid twenties, I changed my name from 'Jacinta' to 'Cindy' in a conscious bid to make it easier for everyone to pronounce and remember me: or so I thought, little realising that I was further suppressing my inner shame and guilt. Inflated by my growing ego, I set up my own Training Consultancy in 1991 with a relentless determination and will to succeed. Facilitating dynamic workshops the length and breadth of England and Ireland, my standards were exceptionally high as I pushed myself mercilessly, without any consideration for my poor body. I did not entertain failure in any way and so Cindy emerged – strong, versatile, tenacious, competitive, impeccably groomed, successful and most of all fiercely driven by demons deep within.

Whilst my working life was where I excelled, and felt in complete control, my personal life was a different matter, fragmented with unfulfilling, unhappy relationships repeated my heart-breaking, wounded dance of childhood. Here I was lost. Socially I appeared to have it all, going off for expensive holidays, meeting up with friends, eating out and so on. But really this was the only way I knew how to live. Hence my life prior to the birth of my son was an uncomfortable medley of two/three days a week in a hotel in some corner of UK or Ireland packed with six hour adrenalin-hyped hard working training days in the spotlight, followed by weary, lonely days at home forcing myself to go out in the evenings under the delusion that I was 'living'. The irony being that Living with myself was the hardest of all.

Towards the end of 1990, a good friend asked me why I continued taking telephone calls from my mother every day or two. These calls were not conversations as such but more alcohol induced, demented monologues from my mother in which she continued to layer further guilt upon me reducing me to tears. If I was lucky I managed to utter the odd 'yes' or 'no'. Having finished with me, she would often then ring my sister and spew out a similar tirade. My sister and I would then console each other later. The only reply I could give my wise friend was:

'I don't know what else to do. I thought I owed mammy this as she is very lonely since daddy died'

Then the penny dropped. Perhaps I didn't need to do this anymore.

I sought a counsellor and very slowly began to feel through my childhood. This led me to making the difficult but vital decision to stop all contact with my mother allowing myself precious 'feeling' time.

My pregnancy and the birth of my beautiful son in 1995 brought an amazing sense of fulfilment, relief and love into my life. My whole world had changed, thank God and for the better. However, I still felt unable even at that stage to let go of my punishing lifestyle, instead pushing myself even harder to manage it all even though my system was aching for rest and commitment to fulfilling motherhood. It was to take much longer for me to wake up, let go and heal.

Eventually seven years later, I reluctantly had to admit to myself that I either needed to reduce my workload or change direction. Cindy was tired and cracks were beginning to show at long last. Although this was very difficult, slow and painful at the time, I am grateful that I was able to make this change. Consequently, I joined a local charity working with vulnerable homeless families in April 2004. I felt completely at home. One month into my new role, I was diagnosed with Breast Cancer.

4

A Toxic Beginning

2004

'I don't want to go down here daddy, I am scared'. Daddy looks sad. 'You must do as your mother says, Cinty. You will be alright down here. You must stay here until I come back for you and on no account come back upstairs.' With tears dropping silently from my eyes, I wave bye bye and clutching my teddy, I slowly clamber down the giant steps into the cellar. The door shuts suddenly behind me, making my little body jump. I know its my fault so I have to stay here. I trust Daddy and don't want to get him into trouble with mammy. My little lungs struggle to breathe in the musty, damp air and the harsh, glaring light pierces my tired, tearful eyes. Shivering and terrified, I root myself on top of a heap of yucky coal in the corner, away from ravenous mice scurrying about beneath my freezing feet. I dig out some coal with my hands, trying hard to make a sort of bed for myself whilst trying to keep my new dress clean, or mammy will get angry again. Comforting movement outside the barred window gradually fades as a cruel hand of darkness descends, making my isolation more terrifying. I feel alone and responsible for the whole world.

20th April 2004:

During a follow-up appointment with my local doctor for hormone replacement therapy, she confirms that my recent womb scan results are fine, as I suspected they would be. She goes on to check my blood pressure, acknowledging that it is superb, in fact the best it has ever been! I attribute this to my radical change in career. She then proceeds to check my breasts. Now my left breast has always been bigger than my right. This has never really concerned me, especially as I had it checked by the Breast Cancer Consultant at the hospital ten years ago just after I gave birth to Josh. The explanation that I was given then was that there was a small cyst, 'probably full of water', and a probable result of hormone imbalance due to my age. (What a cheek!) However I was relieved. The consultant suggested I take Evening Primrose Oil and Vitamin B12 supplements. This was laughable coming from someone who is inclined to adopt a derisory approach to anything remotely alternative. Looking back, I wish that I had looked into this further, as I now understand that hormone imbalance can be considered (although not proven) as one of the possible contributory causes of Breast Cancer. In fact, this consultant's flippant comments actually gave me a false sense of security about my breast.

However, as my doctor feels my left breast, she frowns, observing that it feels very lumpy. She immediately fast tracks me to my local hospital for a mammogram. This is the start of our life changing experience as a family.

22nd April 04: As I do not have a partner as such, I ask my close friend Martin to come with me. As I had an upsetting, uncomfortable experience with an earlier mammogram. I want some company and support on this occasion. I am not really concerned about the results. I feel that my doctor is just taking extra precautions before prescribing Hormone Replacement Therapy.

At the hospital, I change into an oversized gown and wait. I am called in quite quickly. I explain to the radiographer what had happened last time and that I am feeling a little nervous this time. I want to make sure that she fully understands how I am feeling and can see me for 'me' and not merely another patient. Although I do not realise it at the time, this is the start of my 'active' part in my treatment. Something I do as I go along. The radiographer is very understanding and explains the procedure to me before beginning. She then guides me slowly through each stage. Once I know that the radiographer is 'with me', I feel less nervous and not about to be 'done to'. I feel empowered.

Hours pass and suddenly I hear the latch on the door at the top of the cellar steps. Daddy has come for me. I run up the steps with a renewed desperation into daddy's arms. Holding his hand and clutching my teddy, we go back upstairs, my little legs straining to take one stair at a time to keep up with Daddy. He is quiet and looks sad. I hope mammy is not still mad with daddy or me. My insides are all muddled up. I cannot stop shivering. At the top of the stairs, Daddy tells me to go to my room as he solemnly walks back into the kitchen. I wish he would give me a cuddle. I don't know what I have done wrong. I play quietly upstairs alone in my room careful not to make a sound in case I annoy mammy again. I think my brother and sister are in their room playing. I feel left out and not part of what's happening around me. Later, I come down to the kitchen for tea anxious to see mammy's face. She looks serious but not angry. I take a deep breath and tentatively sit down without so much as a whisper. I am afraid to breathe in case I make everything worse all over again. The terrible stuff has passed for now. That evening we all kneel down as a family amongst the day's smouldering ashes and pray. We say the rosary, pretending the bad things are not that bad.

26th April 04: I wait in reception to see the consultant. A nurse quickly shows me into the special waiting area. My name is called out and I am shown in to meet the official looking General Consultant. After examining me, he looks at the mammogram results on an illuminated screen, explaining that there are some calcified cells. I ask what this means. His reply changes my world forever: 'This is a sign of Cancer'. This is the first time that I have heard the word Cancer. It had not even entered my head before this appointment and without any time to take this on board, the consultant sits down behind his desk and immediately continues: 'You will need a biopsy, I will put your name down. The earliest date we have available is…' I cannot speak or catch my breath. I have no time to think or feel. I feel so small, all of a sudden, and very vulnerable. Don't I have a say in what happens to me? Eventually I manage to blurt out from the depth of my shaken body: 'there is a huge difference between my 'needing' a biopsy and my 'deciding if I am going to have one'. Immediately the nurse, who has remained silent up to this point, comes to my side and tries to empathise: 'you are in shock dear'. I feel confused and terrified. I don't know this person. I try to explain that I am terrified of needles. Before I can continue, this very professional looking anonymous nurse abruptly interrupts saying that I have a needle phobia, which she promptly adds to my notes. She quickly shows me to the door. I feel dismissed with overwhelming news. I am in a daze as I wander through reception. The Receptionist tells me that I have to go back to the clinic, as I do not have the correct paperwork. Tears silently drop from my eyes. The Receptionist gently mentions that it doesn't matter and books me in for my biopsy. I leave the hospital, sit in my car and cry and cry and cry.

Why can the consultant not empathise? Is he not human also? It seems to me that the consultant gives the facts and the nurse attempts to give the emotional support! This doesn't work. It is disjointed and too late. Whatever happened to explaining this procedure to me gently, asking how I felt about it and if I was happy about proceeding rather than assuming I will agree? This would have made all the difference.

The glare of the naked light bulb penetrates my sobbing eyes, never leaving me alone. Through the small murky, barred window above, I can see legs of many people walking past on the pavement above, completely unaware of my isolated existence below. I wish daddy would come and take me away from here. Minutes pass painfully slowly, blending into long, scary hours deprived of light and love. What is wrong with me? I don't want to be alone. The fighting upstairs is replaced with sounds of hungry mice down here. I never try to leave because I know daddy will come for me when it is quiet upstairs. As I sit here alone, freezing and frightened, under the piercing, bald light bulb, the raging war upstairs bears down on my small shoulders, deepening my guilt for the problems I have caused.

27th April 04: Holding this unbearable news inside me I rush back from a work meeting to pick up my son from school my mind in turmoil. A speed camera flashes blinding me for a moment capturing me driving at 34 miles per hour. Oh my god, this will bring my total points up to 12. I can't lose my driving licence. How will I get my son to and from school, get myself to radiotherapy eventually in Oxford, attend work meetings around Buckinghamshire and Berkshire. Everything is happening too quickly for me. Having made some calls to my solicitor, I realise quickly that to stand any chance of holding on to my licence, I shall need to present my case myself in court in Oxford. My world is shaking and I am struggling to hold on.

3rd May 04: What am I going to do? I am terrified of needles. I cannot face this biopsy under a local anaesthetic. I feel so alone. I telephone the hospital and ask to speak to the Breast Cancer Consultant himself. Surprisingly he returns my call. I am on my way to work. Hearing my mobile ring, I pull over quickly and stop in a lay-by. I express my deep-rooted fear in absolute detail, hoping he will understand: 'Doctor I was abused as a child and since then I have had a horror of needles. They remind me of my father's abuse'. The line goes silent for a few moments but then he agrees to arrange sedation for me for this procedure. I really appreciate this. I think I can face this procedure, knowing that I shall not be aware of what is happening. I just cannot bear knowing what is happening to me.

A week later, I ask my strongest friend Geraldine if she can come with me to the hospital for this frightening procedure. She agrees and I feel relieved knowing she is there for me. Geraldine is a wonderful lady in her seventies and coping with lung Cancer, although you would never know. She never speaks of her illness. She has remarkable eyes that exude peace and love to everyone. I met Geraldine originally seven years earlier when I attended an adult education course in Meditation. This was my first foray out into the world with my then two-year-old son Josh, the crèche facilities at this college making it possible.

15th May 04: I wake up this morning after a very restless night's sleep, feeling jumpy inside. I don't know what is ahead of me today and that scares me to death. All I am sure of is that Geraldine will be with me and I will be out for the count during this procedure. I don't mind pain when I wake up as long as I am not aware of it during the procedure. Suddenly the doorbell rings and I jump out of my skin. As I open the door, Geraldine's warm smile and loving eyes help me breathe a little easier. Thirty minutes later, we are walking slowly along the long hospital corridor, the fluorescent lights above bearing down heavily. My breathing becomes shallow and erratic, anxiety sucking vital air from my compressed lungs. Reaching the meagrely furnished waiting room, I tentatively sit down barely touching the seat. 'Jacinta McShane please' perforates my eardrums. Before I know it, I am standing rooted to the spot, frozen in terror.

Suddenly, all the air leaves my body, I can't breathe, my body stiffens as if in spasm. Daddy's dinner is sliding painfully down the stained kitchen wall. I run away to hide behind the big armchair in the corner pushing my ears into my head until my hands turn white, trying so hard to block out the awful noise. Poor daddy, he never gets his dinner. The arguing goes on and on. I cannot see Deirdre or Gerard. Mammy looks fierce like she is going to burst, her bazookas blazing. Daddy isn't saying anything. He never says anything. But why? No matter how I try, this terrible sound pierces my whole body. I come out screaming and crying from behind the chair: 'Stop, Stop, Stop, Stop'! My heart blows up inside me. Mammy orders daddy: 'Take that child down to the cellar out of my bloody sight' It is all my fault. It is always all my fault. No matter what I do, it is still always my fault. Why! Why! Why does Daddy do what mammy tells him to do when it hurts me?

Geraldine offers to come in with me. I beg her not to leave me for a second no matter what anyone says. She promises to stay with me throughout the complete procedure much to the irritation of the medical staff concerned. As I come around, my friend Geraldine is there beside me still and constant in her support.

26th May 04: Today I am off to see the General Consultant whom I saw originally. A nurse shows us into a plain, clinical looking room, asking me if I had come for a biopsy. She has forgotten who I am, which only exacerbates my growing anxiety. She quietly disappears into the adjoining office. I can hear a man's voice, presumably the consultant, speaking to someone on the phone. Meanwhile my friend Martin is talking to me about something completely unrelated but I am only half-listening, as I am curious to know what is going on next door. Then I hear a man's voice asking 'Where are her results?' His next words catapult me into the far office wall. 'Oh I see, so then a full mastectomy would be best?' My friend Martin holds me as I fall to pieces inside. A terrifying blackness devours me. Gasping for air, I hear the door open and the nurse's words: 'Oh dear, she is not taking it too well!' Out of my terror, I want to punch this nurse but am unable to move. Her insensitivity only makes my diagnosis so much harder to bear.

Once I catch my breath, the consultant clinically explains the situation and wants to put me down for a mastectomy, the removal of my right breast. I cannot make a decision of this magnitude here and now. I immediately ask to see the Breast Cancer Consultant for another opinion and decline surgery at this time. I appreciate that these doctors and nurses see hundreds of patients each day with similar problems, but I am not 'hundreds', I am 'me' – a single mum facing a potentially life-threatening illness with my own concerns and expectations. I want to be treated as a person (not a number), with sensitivity and respect. This experience starts my long journey to gaining 'personal' treatment within the National Health Service – everyone's right as outlined in the National Health Service Plan and more specifically within the Patient Advice and Liaison Service initiative. As we leave this cold-hearted place, I cannot stop crying. I sob into the hallway wall, at which point one of the Breast Care Nurses guides us both to a little room upstairs. I was to visit this 'consoling' room many times over the next few months.

28th May 04: I do not hesitate in contacting Patient Advice and Liaison Service at the hospital after my dreadful experience. I already knew Nick – the Patient Advice and Liaison Service manager, from my training days. I telephone him and explain my situation, asking him to intervene for me. I want the Breast Cancer Consultant to be made fully aware of what I have experienced. I need to be reassured that this will not happen again. Also I do not want to have to handle this all myself, in addition to trying to cope with my diagnosis. Nick seems to understand the help that I need without being patronising in any way. At least, all my training work has helped me know how to access Patient Advice and Liaison Service. Now I can see it actually working for me.

It's Sunday afternoon and daddy takes us all for a walk along the quay by Lough Foyle, just ten minutes walk from our home in Shipquay. I love this time with Daddy. Mammy is not here to take him away from us. Daddy is quiet but a little more chatty than when he is with mammy. He knows about a lot of things and I love hearing him talk about all sorts. He shows us the big, commercial ships moored along the quay, one is a dredger and another is a coal ship. I hate going back home and don't want our times together to end. I want more time with Daddy. I always want more of Daddy's time. My whole body tenses as we approach our home, shrouded in darkness.

30th May 04: This time, I am not taking any chances. I need support so I am bringing Annie and my friend Geraldine with me to my next appointment with the Breast Cancer Consultant. He comes in and introduces himself to me, quietly telling me that he knows my situation (so I know the Patient Advice and Liaison Service has intervened.). Everyone takes up their positions. The consultant sits on one side of his desk, I sit on the other, Annie positions herself at the corner of the desk, and my friend Geraldine sits alongside me. Then the Breast Care Nurse comes in and stands behind my friend Geraldine and I. On top of this, 'that nurse' comes in from time to time, hovering around us. My goodness, I cannot help wonder if this is all for my good, in case I get 'emotional' again. Alternatively, is this intervention in case I involve PALS again!

The usual ominous signs appear. As mammy's face intensifies, a dark foreboding cloud descends. Mammy's dark expression and argumentative behaviour betrays the alcoholic secret in her teacup. Slowly but surely whisky is transforming my mother into a monster capable of physical violence and foul language laced with accusations, threats and insults. We fall into our respective defence positions, my father taking her abuse and trying in vain to pacify her, my brother leaving the house, my little sister disappearing into a corner and myself preparing to look out for daddy and pick up the pieces after mammy has finished with him. The more mammy drinks the more she seems to hate us all. I don't understand. I want to understand. As I strain to listen at the bottom of the stairs, I can faintly hear frantic ramblings emanating from her bedroom, all absorbed by daddy who, sitting by her bedside, listens resignedly for hours on end, his hands turning blue with the chilling atmosphere. He finally reappears, life drained from his face, worn down by her endless battering. 'What's wrong with mammy?' I ask, earnestly looking for some believable explanation. 'Your mum is just poorly. Its her time of the month.' My heart sinks again. How I wish daddy would tell me the truth. I know this is all wrong. Why won't he just tell me the truth? 'Would you like some tea, Daddy?'

30th May 04: Lying on the bed in the small room next to the Consultant's office, he feels my lumpy breast and suggests that he aspirates another cyst with a needle to check if it's cancerous. I sit up with a start, gasping for air, and scream: 'No No, No'. I am terrified of needles. The consultant quickly disappears into the next room and the nurse helps me recover. I join my friends next door and the consultant explains that it may not be necessary to remove my whole breast. He suggests I have a lumpectomy with first stage lymph node removal. Unfortunately for me, the procedure called 'Sentinel Node Biopsy' is not in operation at this stage. (A procedure, as I understand it, whereby they inject a dye into the lymph nodes, highlighting those nodes, if any, through which the Cancer may be travelling). Hence first stage removal, as I understand it, means having approximately nine or so nodes nearest the lump removed, which should not weaken my arm too much. He then repeats that he can now do a small needle aspiration to ascertain if another little cyst is cancerous. I feel panicky yet again. His unfortunate choice of words only increases my anxiety: 'Don't worry, we will just 'pop' a needle in and take some fluid' There it is again: 'pop a needle in' Oh my God! "It may be a 'pop' to you but it's trauma for me' I manage to reply. Perhaps this is his awkward attempt at lightening the whole procedure. Instead this consultant's flippancy only heightens my anxiety. It is so important to me that whoever is treating me understands and respects my fear. I decline the offer of a needle aspiration, out of sheer terror. I manage to agree to have a lumpectomy and lymph node removal.

This whole meeting stuns me and shakes me to the core. I have so many more questions.

My little ears, glued to my sister and brother's upstairs bedroom door are hearing something they shouldn't – boing, boing, boing sounds mingled with mammy's and Uncle Jack's giggling. All of a sudden the huge wooden bedroom door springs open and Uncle Jack glares down at me with a strange look in his eyes. I know a secret and can't help giggling. Uncle Jack's eyes darken. My fun quickly turns to fear. I dash into my bedroom opposite and climbing into my bed, I bury myself under the sheets wishing I would disappear. Curled up in the smallest ball imaginable and scarcely breathing, I lie still, my tiny hands holding my eyelids tightly shut. In seconds, my protective sheets are stripped away leaving me cruelly exposed to Uncle Jack's snorting and thundering rant: 'I don't know what you think you know, Cinty, but don't you dare breathe a word to anyone or I will make sure that you pay'. His nostrils bigger, his breathing heavier, his massive body devours me – total blackness.

31st May 04: I have never had an operation in my life and here I am about to go in for serious surgery with uncertain consequences. I cannot see any light at all at the end of this tunnel. My whole world is changing and how am I going to explain all this to my poor little boy. I am his whole world. What assurances can I give him? I do not know how I am going to get through this. All I can see is death! I do not believe that I am going to survive surgery, never mind Cancer. I feel lost and so alone, even though there are good friends around me.

Sitting in our old kitchen (where we do everything), mammy is getting the tea ready. Daddy comes up from his office. I am so excited to see him. He looks tired. He always looks tired. We sit down at the table and start chatting, all at the same time. I can't tell what is on our plates except that it looks burnt. Mammy is not a great cook. Daddy says something and suddenly all hell breaks loose again. I am sad not knowing what will happen next nor whom to turn to for help. I have to go down to the cold cellar again. Why me, only me? Why can't my brother or sister come with me? Struggling to keep up with Daddy, I jump from one step to the other as we slowly go downstairs. Daddy opens the door revealing steep, stone steps stretching into the darkness below. 'I don't want to go down here Daddy, I am frightened and cold.'. Daddy looks sad. 'At the bottom of the stone steps, to the right in one corner there is a large pile of coke. To the left, a pile of coal climbs up the clammy, dark wall. Next to this, a pile of damp slack. Ahead of me, the cellar opens out into a large stone-walled room with a huge mound of coal against the wall, a glaring, naked light bulb above and to the left a long rectangular shaped window with bars. This is where the fighting stops for now. I know that there are rats and mice down here sometimes. Daddy often puts out some traps with bits of stale cheese, returning later to find the rats and mice dead, their bloody heads caught under the trap wire. I try to sleep now and again forcing this nightmare from my mind but the bare light bulb overhead is always on, staring down at me, never leaving me alone.

1st June 04: For those first dreadful forty-eight hours after diagnosis, Josh and I stay with friends, both of whom happen to be counsellors. They look after us, Josh having friends to play with whilst I break into pieces, clinging to my friends at times for love and life itself. I feel lost and alone, unsure of what is happening to me and what is happening inside me. There is a broken child inside my dis-eased adult body, shaken and unsure of whom to trust, believing she is going to die. How can I help her?

A couple of days later, I have a day off work, so I suppose I ought to do some food shopping as the fridge is looking sadly bare. I find myself wandering around town. What was my normal life now feels surreal. Instead my impending surgery, treatment and death feel real. I walk into Tesco and emerge later with a few bags of food but I don't know how I managed that as I cannot recall anything. I don't want to go back home. I do not want to face an empty house. Somehow I have to find some peace so that I can be there for my darling Josh when he comes home from school. Everyone around me seems to be getting on with their lives, yet mine has suddenly come to a grinding halt.

Gerard, Deirdre and I are playing on the street outside our house. I always feel separate from them, not really part of their fun. They seem to have each other and I don't fit in. Our big front door opens and I see Daddy. As I run over to him, mammy appears at the door too and stops me talking to him. I am disappointed. I stand beside their legs patiently waiting for my turn. Mammy looks very serious with her two mounted bazookas blocking my view. They are arguing. I am hoping Daddy will give me a cuddle in a minute but Mammy won't let this happen and I don't know why. I feel that I don't matter. They do not really see me.

3rd June 04: Where can I go to for help? Then, without being consciously aware of what I am doing, I start walking towards my local church – St. Mary's C of E in Aylesbury. I know Canon Tim Higgins through my work with the homeless. I wander in and ask someone working there if I can speak to Tim. Tim kindly comes over to see me from his home. I am in bits, completely panicking, without anything to hold on to. I ask him to help me but I do not know how he can. I am so worried about Josh. What will happen to my boy? Who will look after him? Tim is so steady. He listens to me and seems to understand, although I don't know how. I hardly make any sense. I feel as if I am at sea, unable to swim and there is no rescue in sight. I just need someone I can trust. This is my way to God although I do not realise it. Tim assures me that he will come in to see me in hospital before and after the operation. I hear the word 'after' not really believing I will be here, but it helps in a strange way. Tim promises to hold a special service for me in their little church. I am glad of all the help I can get. This lovely man becomes solid for Josh and I through our turbulent journey and St. Mary's Church becomes a second home[1].

Sunday morning and our battered little family are all getting ready for our weekly public display of family unity at midday mass at our Cathedral in Derry. As far as I can tell, God has very little to do with all this. For mammy, this is a chance to dress up in all her finery and show us off to her

---

[1] See appendix A at back of this book for more information. St. Mary's Church in Aylesbury provide a valuable 'space' programme to help others in distress.

friends at church. For daddy, this is a more sombre affair. For me, I am on my best behaviour, a broad grin plastered religiously across my face, successfully hiding my uncertainty and insecurity. This is mammy's show and we all fall in line, trailing in her wake. First mammy, her bazookas standing proud, then daddy followed by myself, my brother and sister file into this imposing edifice, slowly making our way to our habitual pew, five rows from the altar at the front and on the right side of the aisle. Daddy kneels and prays, mammy looks around to see who she knows and what they are wearing and I mouth the confusing, Latin words and follow what daddy does. Surrounded by the huge, coloured leaden windows, the frozen stares of the cold, marble statues peer down at me. The sacrificial starkness of the ornate altar decked in white, bearing two tall, rigid candles beckons me. Amongst all these people, I feel smaller and more lost than ever.

5

Getting To Know My Cancer

5th June 04: Since this nightmare began in May this year, I feel lost and vulnerable, swept off my feet by a fierce, formidable thunderstorm, with no sense of direction and no hope of getting out. I have lost all control. I am not sure why exactly but I know that I need to understand my Cancer, to stand any chance of living through this nightmare.

When I was first diagnosed, I could not take in the detail of that meeting, not to mention understand it. When I was offered chemotherapy, radiotherapy and hormone blocker drugs in one meeting with an oncologist whom I did not know, I could not take in and understand what these treatments really involved and how they worked. I was devastated by my diagnosis and reeling from four operations and four general anaesthetics. There is so much that I need to know. I have so many questions. It is very hard sometimes asking these questions while feeling so vulnerable and always tired. In some ways it would be easier for me not to question but go along passively with what doctors suggest, but there is a little voice inside me yearning to be heard and wanting to speak out. My little child wants to live this time. Slowly but surely I voice my thoughts and feelings and begin to claw my way back from 'hurt and shame' and slowly start to reclaim this beautiful, gentle, innocent part of me. If I were to ignore my inner voice this time, I would be allowing myself to be abused by the very health system that is treating me. Asking questions is key to helping myself regain some control over what is happening to me.

I have so many questions:

Why am I treated for this disease as if I am not part of it?

Why is it assumed that I will have treatment?

Why do I need my breast removed?

How do you know the Cancer is just here in my breast?

What is a tumour?

What size is the tumour?

Can I be sedated for the biopsy?

How can you clear it completely?

What does 'invasive' mean exactly?

What is HER2?

What do you mean by 'as far as you know'

What is chemotherapy?

What does oncology mean?

What are the side-effects in the short and long-term?

What are the chances of my Cancer returning after chemotherapy?

How does radiotherapy work?

What are the side-effects in the short and long term?

Why am I not informed about suitable Cancer drugs even if they are not available on the National Health Service?

Why is it assumed that I understand what is going on?

Can I have copies of my blood tests, CT scans?

Why can I not see the same consultant as before?

Why does my file carry the description 'anxious and emotional' patient?

Why does my file not carry the words: 'assertive and challenging' patient?

How will I manage to keep working, keep my home going and look after my boy all at the same time as having Cancer?

How will I keep up payments on my home?

How can I have time to be sick?

Who will look after Josh if I should die?

Who will look after Josh when I go into hospital?

What state benefits am I entitled to?

How do I get these benefits without stress and hassle?

How do I cope?

I do not feel that our health system genuinely encourages patients to question doctors', consultants', oncologists' diagnosis, suggestions, advice. There seems to be a lot of assumptions made, for instance the assumption that I understand what I am being told, the assumption that I will have treatment, the assumption that I am coping, and so on. There does not appear to be enough time. I am astonished and angry with some of the attitudes of the doctors and consultants that I am experiencing as a patient – attitudes of arrogance, superiority and patronage, which can only serve to perpetuate the gross imbalance in doctor/patient power. I want to be treated as Jacinta – the individual first and foremost, who happens to have Breast Cancer. After all, I have been on this planet for 52 years before Cancer came into my life. When I come into hospital, ALL of me comes in, not just my Cancer. I want to understand my dis-ease and look into the full range of medical and complementary treatments available so that I can make informed choices, ensuring that I am doing the best for my son and myself. I insist on being fully involved in this way. I am a big part of this healing process, after all. Perhaps this way I can get a handle on what is happening and perhaps then it will stop happening to me.

My following poem is addressed to health professionals and sums up my thoughts as a person who has Cancer.

'We are in this Together'

'I am not a breast
I am not Breast Cancer
I am not a patient
I am a person
just like you
with my own home
family and career
just like you!
my own thoughts and opinions,
concerns and anxieties
just like you!
Please treat 'all of me'
We are in this together!

6

Still Alive!

Daddy is always busy working downstairs in the bank. I love going down to his big office and spending time with him, just the two of us. I know he has lots of work to do. I bring my homework 'cos Daddy likes helping me with my Maths and Latin. I sit up at the cashier's desk feeling very important and start working whilst Daddy works at his desk. This is great. Daddy then takes some papers and puts them in the huge, steel safe. It's even bigger than me. I love this special time with Daddy. I have him all to myself.

10th June 04: This morning before going to school, Josh gives me a special prayer written by his class for me to take to hospital.

Dear Lord

Please make sure you are looking over Josh's mum. Please make sure she gets well soon because she is a wonderful person. Also make sure that Josh is happy and safe while his mum is recovering.

When Josh's mum comes out of hospital, help her get the rest she needs and encourage their friends to look after her and Josh during this time.

Thank-you for listening to us.

Amen

Emerald class

Collaborative prayer 10. 6. 04

This brings more tears to my eyes. My very brave little boy. He then goes to school as usual, yet everything is as far from usual as we have ever experienced. Before leaving home for the hospital, I have written out a will and insist that my friend Claire reads it and signs it. I do not believe that I will be coming home again.

We arrive at the hospital and make our way to the surgical ward. A very long wait in the waiting room intensifies my stress and deepens my fear. Claire just stays close to me. I really appreciate her not trying to tell me that it will be all right and to calm down. Her silent reassuring presence is all I need. We are shown into a small private room, which is where I will stay for the first night. This is all so new to me. I had never been in hospital except to have my son Josh. So much uncertainty. A young nurse begins asking me for my name, address. She asks me to remove jewellery, nail polish, make-up. I feel as if I am about to be imprisoned. I have to hand over my few remaining comforts and marks of personal identification. I have been depersonalised and am now a patient number. I wish hospital staff would tell me their names first, it would make me feel more at ease. The anaesthetist arrives next. I do not know him either. He speaks to me formally as well. I explain again that I am terrified of injections. In fact I am afraid of everything at this moment. Claire comes with me to theatre and comes into the pre-operating room, staying with me until the anaesthetic takes effect. I am so grateful she is with me.

Sitting round the fire as New Year's Eve approaches with an almost unbearable certainty, mum's face darkens as each minute slowly passes. I hold my breath as if to prevent the inevitable. Mum is changing before my eyes becoming the most foreboding spectre. Daddy just sits there helpless. I watch the minute hand of the clock, trying so hard to slow it down, but it ticks steadily and relentlessly moving towards the end of my world. What is she thinking? What have I done wrong? Why is midnight so bad? Mammy's anger spews out in all directions with a terrible force. I cannot get away. Daddy be careful! Mammy lunges at him with an empty whisky bottle. I cannot bear to look. The rest is a blur. My world is broken into small pieces.

Several hours later, I wake up in my room feeling sore and groggy but absolutely amazed and exhilarated to be alive. I am alive. I can survive surgery! I didn't know I could. Claire is beside me. I want to see Josh. The next thing I know, Claire has disappeared and my friend Angie and Josh are beside me. It's like magic. I am so glad to see my boy. I must have made it. 'It was strange when I first came in, seeing all the people walking around with nurses behind them and tubes in them. It was strange seeing a ward for the first time. And then going into the room with all the machinery and seeing you in bed with the tubes and the room was quite dark.' whispers Josh. I try to reassure him but his little words slip gently away as I drift off again.

Mammy and Daddy start fighting all over again, only this time louder and louder. I am terrified of what might happen next. Suddenly, one of my lungs, unable to bear this pain any longer, collapses, sucking vital air from my young, unloved body. I cannot breathe. Just fifteen years old, I feel I am dying. A doctor stands over my bed at home, telling my mother that I have to go into the old chest hospital. My sad father, my unpredictable mother, my little brother and sister all slowly fading into nothingness. I am plunged into a cold, clinical world amass with strangers in white coats prodding and poking my lifeless body, talking over me as if I am not here. Endless rows of old iron, rickety patient beds giving out pungent odours of the sickly: doleful groans and death knells engulf me. Trapped and terrified, a slow rising panic devours me. Let me out. Let me out. I languish here, my young life suspended for two months, an awkward rest replacing my mother's psychotic episodes. So many old people here, friendly but poorly, coughing and wailing day and night invading my unsettled sleep. Today I am wheeled to theatre. I don't know why. Where is daddy? This dimly lit stark room hides an ominous secret. Faceless bodies surround me peering over their cold blue masks. Sitting me upright, wrapped around an ice-cold metal chair and holding me down, a large needle suddenly pierces my frozen back. My whole body screams, panic and terror taking me over. Darkness consumes me. I start falling. Not again. Help me please someone, anyone.

I wake up sobbing inconsolably in my hospital bed. My mother beside me. I failed. The doctors could not do the lumbar puncture. I was hysterical and now it is my fault. I don't want to do it. Mum seems annoyed. I beg her not to make me. Before I know it, a nurse starts tilting my bed so that my head is nearly touching the floor and my feet are higher in the air. A long tube forces its way up my nose and way down my throat – my sickening alternative to theatre. I want to be sick. Mammy has left. As fluid passes through this long tube reaching the pit of my stomach, my body heaves and coughs up murky gunge from my 'bloody' home. The weeks stretch slowly before me, my body slowly emptying itself and my weary lung eventually reluctantly inflating in preparation for my return to my unhappy life. A few days go by as I slowly regain my strength. My face drops as mammy arrives to take me home. She speaks to the consultant first but seems engrossed in impressing him, falling back on her artificial, posh voice. Where is daddy? Why couldn't he come to take me home instead? Daddy is never around when I need him. He never holds me anymore. I miss him so much.

Not wanting to leave nor wanting to stay, an omen perhaps of worse to come. Leaving the hospital, the taxi driver asks mammy for the address. '57, Limavady Road', mammy replies. 'Are we going somewhere else first before going home? I ask curiously. Then mammy drops a bombshell. 'We are going to your new home. Your father has retired and we left the Bank House while you were in hospital.' I cannot take this in. 'What about all my things, my clothes, my books and everything?' I ask anxiously, a slow panic rising from the pit of my stomach. 'Don't overreact Cinty, I threw out what you won't need and packed the rest of your things and they are at your new home.' I have not had a chance to say goodbye. Everything has disappeared cos I have been ill. Nothing stays the same. I don't belong anywhere.

15th June 04: I am surprised to find myself reluctant to leave hospital after my lumpectomy. I have survived my operation and feel very relieved to be still here. I am getting such a much-needed rest. Josh is safe and looked after. All my meals are being served to me. I can take all day, trying to turn over in bed if I want to. Sheer heaven! My friend Simon is here to collect me from hospital. Poor man, he looks worse than I feel. He is worried and I am relieved. On leaving the hospital, I mention that I want to go to Hartwell House – a beautiful historic hotel near my home, and sit in the grounds with a glass of white wine. I want to celebrate first, and then I can go home and recover.

Simon looks even whiter if that's possible. Hey, I am alive again. I want to celebrate.

Following this surgery, my breast becomes swollen and looks black and blue. It does not hurt really so I can live with it. The hardest part of all this is sleeping alone in bed at night. Most of my wonderful support ends at our front door. Simon is kindly staying with us for a week, which is just brilliant. Inside our home, it is usually just Josh and myself. I want to protect him so much but this noble intention only piles on the pressure. I am so frightened that something will happen to me in bed at night. I get the odd sudden pain, which wakes me up, with a jolt. I am trying so hard to hide my tears and fears from Josh. I did not know I could cry so much. Speaking to my friend Sue in Wales who has been through breast Cancer herself, reassures me a little. It isn't till later that I realise that she experienced similar swelling and discolouration, resulting in her breast actually bursting during the night. I am so grateful that she did not share this with me at the time. I don't know how I would have coped.

A detached white and black Victorian house on the far side of town looks at me strangely. A sudden realisation that this was to be my new home rips through my frail body. Mammy's bazookas protruding out in front lead the way into this vacuous edifice called home. Daddy and my brother and sister are inside. Daddy has retired without telling me. This house is so different to our Bank House. It only has nine rooms and is so much smaller. Gerard and Deirdre sleep in the same bedroom, mammy and daddy have separate bedrooms and I have my own room. Devoid of central heating, relying on coal fires and an Aga in the kitchen for warmth, the house has a permanent underlying coldness, sucking out the inadequate heating. Everything is different here, daddy is no longer working and the bank is no longer downstairs, mammy has not got a clue how to run a house without a housekeeper and porter to rely upon. We are all at sea in an uncomfortable way.

After a few days in this new house that is supposed to be home, I get the bus into town, intent on returning to our old Bank house to say my final good-byes. Everything has changed here too. I struggle to take in what has happened to our home. The bedrooms, the living room we used to play in, mammy's posh drawing room, the pantry I used to hide in, even the battered kitchen replaced with impersonal, functional offices. All signs of hell that was home snuffed out in an instant without warning, transformed into office after office after office. How could all this have happened whilst I was sick in hospital?

8th July 04: A couple of days after my second operation, I am starting to feel brighter although sore and fragile. It is mid morning as I lie in bed. The hustle and bustle of nursing staff running around signals the arrival of doctors (a hospital's 'higher power') doing their rounds. I cannot believe how many doctors with junior/trainee doctors following in their wake, come on to the ward at the same time. There are eight of us patients but actually as many as ten in their entourage. Is this about empowering the patient or empowering the medical team? Ten doctors and trainees surround my bed. I feel dwarfed by their presence. Imagine – there I am feeling poorly, sore, vulnerable and fragile and ten medical staff descend on me, encircling my bed, most of whom I have never seen before, nor do they introduce themselves to me. Towering over me, one doctor asks the diminutive, lowly nurse how is the patient doing (as if I am not even there)! Well all of me is here, not just my stitched breast.

How can this behaviour possibly empower the patient? If only, doctors would take a moment to see things from the patient's viewpoint, then I am sure their manner would be warmer and patients would react more favourably. After all, we are all human, regardless of our position.

Hospital Ward **by Josh**

Josh captures my ward perfectly in this picture. I am amazed by his attention to detail in these circumstances. I am so glad that he has been able to put his thoughts into sketches.

18th July 04: This time, after my third operation to remove more tissue, in order to try to get a clear margin around the original tumour, I walk into hospital prepared for bad news. The waiting room is quiet. My friend Martin is with me this time. We are called in quite quickly to see another breast cancer consultant. He has a quick look at my breast, going on to explain that some of the margin is clear (at least I receive some good news first, which helps) but they had found some more invasive Cancer cells – no surprise there then. I ask to read the report, which he shows me and surprisingly agrees to give me a copy. He suggests that I definitely need to have a mastectomy, to which I agree. I have now reached the point where I am less frightened of losing my breast than of the Cancer spreading. As far as they know, it hasn't spread! I hear this phrase 'As far as they know' alarmingly often. It is not at all reassuring. I feel very upset. Even though I am prepared for this, it still hits hard. It's not so much the surgery itself but the emotional loss of my breast. I find this consultant understanding and reasonably empathetic. He then talks about rebuilding my breast. Again I am offered reconstructive surgery. I find it amazing how easily this procedure is mentioned. From what I have read, this is major surgery and quite an ordeal to put my body through for essentially cosmetic reasons. Having said that, this consultant does not feel it would be wise for me to have a rebuild on this occasion, after all the surgery I have had so far. I completely agree. Psychologically I need to come to terms with losing my breast, which is much more important to me than having an immediate replacement. At last, some consideration for the rest of me. I do wonder about the effect of two general anaesthetics and the trauma of further operations on my body and my already depleted immune system. I would have thought that it would be important to bolster my immune system as much as possible during this time. But then, what do I know: I am only the patient!

The Breast Care Nurse then asks Martin and myself if we want to go upstairs, to the little 'consoling' room, as I call it, to talk some more. I am very upset and agree. I find one particular Breast Care Nurse less understanding than the other. It feels to me as if her own agenda comes into play more than it should, leaving me feeling that she is not really empathising with me but doing her job. She starts showing me what I could wear in the form of padding in my bra when leaving the hospital after my surgery and then talks about having a prosthesis fitted. I am not ready to consider these options at this stage. I am too upset and just want her to understand how I am feeling, and perhaps mention how other patients often feel the same way. However, another Breast Care Nurse is much more understanding and is able to listen attentively to my concerns which is very helpful and supportive.

The hardest part of all this is not so much going in for my mastectomy but having this surgery knowing that there is probably chemotherapy to follow, that 'may' work. This disease certainly tests what you are really made of as you have to draw upon all your (already depleted) resources to get through it. I now feel and express that I would like a doctor to sit down with me and explain this report to me in plain english, so that I can understand it properly. Having agreed to this third operation, I then change my mind shortly before surgery. I want the consultant to take a wider margin to see if we can get a clear margin this time. I guess that I am just not ready to lose my breast yet.

7th August 04: After this operation to remove a little more tissue from my breast, I am in hospital for about four days recovering. I am getting used to this. I share a ward with five other patients, one of whom is a very elderly lady whom I understand to be suffering from a form of dementia. She has the bed next to mine. At night I pull the curtain around my bed in a vague attempt to keep out the constant light and noise. Each night about one in the morning, I hear a slight stirring coming from the bed next to mine – she is on the move again! Slowly but surely, a little pair of white-socked feet emerges below the curtain and starts travelling gingerly along the ward. This seems to happen each night. This poor lady tends to sleep most of the day and then is awake most of the night, rambling around the ward, not knowing where she is. Why is she on an open ward like this? It cannot be safe for her or others. If it weren't so potentially serious, it would be quite funny in a perverse sort of way. This night however is different – these tiny 'socked' feet move in my direction! When I look down, there she is trying to open my suitcase, which is just under my bed. I get such a shock, As I lean over quickly and pull my case out of her way (with my good arm, I hasten to add), lo and behold, she proceeds to pull up her nightie, pull down her knickers and promptly wee on the floor next to my bed! It then dawns on me that she probably was going to pee in my suitcase (thinking it was a commode). Thank goodness, I reacted quickly. She then continues on her walkabout leaving a large puddle of pungent urine next to my bed! I am speechless! Once I recover a little, I call the night nurse who then rushes after her. I fall asleep. And there the puddle remains until the next morning when another patient anxiously asks a nurse to clean it up. For the rest of my stay, I cautiously hide my fluid drain from any potential threat. I am terrified she might pull it out or worse!

7th September 04: Today I need to see my local doctor for an unrelated matter. Unfortunately my usual doctor is not there. I see one of the other doctors in the practice – a lovely lady, I might add. After examining my sore throat, she surprisingly utters: 'If I were you Jacinta, I would put your feelings to one side and have every treatment you are offered'. This doctor is very kind and compassionate and her advice is definitely well-intentioned, albeit inappropriate for me. I have spent all my life accessing my suppressed feelings and I am not about to let go of them now. This is a vital part of my healing! At the moment, the key to coping with, and finding healing through my Cancer, is expressing clearly how I feel as I go along, gaining a balance between medical and wholistic treatment, in addition to making major life adjustments to ease toxic stress. Listening to my innermost feelings helps me realise what treatments I can cope with. I believe that this gives those treatments the greatest chance of doing me good. Similarly I believe that those treatments that I find difficult and traumatic exert a greater strain on my already weakened immune system, hence affecting the actual benefit of the treatment.

Mammy and Daddy are fighting again. So much noise and terrible words, I am sad and frightened of what might happen. I cannot go to sleep as the awful fighting downstairs gets louder and louder, crashing into my bedroom. Nowhere is safe. Desperate to run away, I rush to the small toilet next door to my room and climb over the toilet on to the small window behind it. There I curl up into the smallest ball imaginable. Squeezing my head in a vain attempt to block out all the noise downstairs, I turn into myself so that I cannot be seen. Even when I am found, I still cannot be seen, not really.

8th September 04: I am getting ready to have my mastectomy in three weeks time. Josh is starting back at school after the summer holiday. He is now in his final year before going to secondary school. When he gets home from his first day back, he casually mentions that his friend did not have a good summer. His mum died from Breast Cancer. Then the penny drops. Oh my god, this is just too close to home. How am I going to handle this? Brushing it under the table is just not an option. Then my beautiful, brave boy's next words break my heart: 'Mum I have an aunt Deirdre in Ireland and an uncle Gerard in America and I don't want to live with either of them. I want to stay in England' How much more does this little boy have to face at this tender age! Then my words just flow without any thought needed at all: 'Darling, at this moment, I am right here' I do not know anymore than that. I gently reassure him about staying at home here in England.

The next day I have a meeting with the Patient advice and Liaison Service Manager. He knows me first and foremost as a person, in my capacity as PALS Training Consultant before I was diagnosed with Breast Cancer. It feels good to be spoken to as a person, not just as a Cancer patient. He gives me information on a special conference in Liverpool in November for Cancer patients, carers and National Health Service professionals. This interests me greatly as I feel that I can contribute, particularly as I come from both sides of the fence, as it were. My only concern is whether it is much too soon for me to do so. Perhaps by November, I will feel more able and confident about doing so. In fact, it was another year and a half before I was really ready to speak anywhere about what Josh and I had experienced as a family.

After my meeting with the Patient Advice and Liaison Service, I go on to The Breast Cancer Advisory Meeting at the hospice next to the hospital. I immediately feel vulnerable walking in. I feel that I am entering the whole new world of Cancer. I meet other ladies with Breast Cancer. We all sit round having tea. A lovely looking young woman in her thirties, sits down beside me and asks me if I would help by completing a brief questionnaire. She explains that this is part of her nursing training. She also has Breast Cancer. I wearily complete the questionnaire but am not really interested in these types of questions. This questionnaire focuses on questions concerning such factors as family history of Breast Cancer, Hormone Replacement Therapy, contraceptive pill, childbirth late in life. I know this information indicates a patient's predisposition to Breast Cancer. I am more interested in psychological factors such as unresolved past traumas, stressful situations, suppressed emotions.

After I got over the initial shock of my diagnosis, I knew without a doubt why Cancer had come to me. God looked down from above and saw that I was making headway with my recovery from childhood, which seemed to affect every part of my life. He saw that I needed a bit of a push forward, so it had to be an illness with long-term consequences, otherwise I could revert to my old ways – hence Cancer. This did not feel like a punishment. On the contrary, it was my healing. I knew this in my heart although I did not understand how this could be. As one nutritionist insightfully said to me early in 2004, after I had explained how I lived: 'If you didn't have Cancer, I would be very surprised!' I see the development of my Cancer quite clearly. My predisposition to Cancer was set in my traumatic childhood, paving the way for denial of my real self throughout life. Consequently, my immune system was weakened, allowing Cancer to take hold. My difficult and reluctant return to work full-time, after the birth of Josh in 1995, put on extra pressure, and my complete change of career nine years later opened up the pathway for Cancer to emerge.

One of the Breast Care Nurses calls me into her office. To my surprise she pulls up my last post-operative report on line and explains it to me in English. This helps enormously, as I can now ask more questions, helping me further understand my Cancer. Little do I realise the steep learning curve I am embarking upon. I want to know and understand all of it, each and every step of the gruelling way.

We are all shown into another room. The nurse proudly explains that they have a breast cancer patient here today who, after having a mastectomy, has had reconstructive surgery which is the best she has ever seen. Nothing prepares me for what I am about to see. Remember, at this stage I have not had my mastectomy. This is all too much and much too soon for me. The same lovely lady in her thirties happily removes her top and stands there proudly and obviously thrilled with her two breasts (as opposed to one). All I can see is a scar line across the top of her right breast. I ask her what that mark is. She explains matter of factly that this is her mastectomy scar, which the surgeons had reopened in order to re-stitch her new breast, to minimise scarring. I am gob-smacked. I cannot take my eyes off this long, long scar, which is soon going to be on me! I then pipe up again asking her if she can feel her new breast, to which she shakes her head. I cannot understand the point of having it there if you cannot feel it. I am curious to feel it myself but I wisely resist. I feel like a little kid listening to a big grown-up. I notice that I am the only one asking questions. Then I have to ask yet another question. 'Where is your nipple on your new breast?' to which this lady confidently replies: 'It will be coming later'. I can't understand what she means, so I have to ask: 'What do you mean?' I look at her in disbelief when she tells me that it will be a tattoo. I try so hard to suppress my urge to roar with laughter. I cannot understand why she would want something she cannot feel that does not have a real nipple. Then one more question bursts out of me: 'Why did you want to have this reconstructive surgery? To which she replies: 'So that I can swim with my children'. I can understand this and see where she is coming from, as she is a young woman in her early thirties and much younger than me. But, to be honest, I want to hear about mastectomy surgery, chemotherapy and Breast Cancer itself. If it is as simple as having a new breast no matter what it looks like, I will have it. But I know that Cancer is the real issue for me, not whether I have a breast or not.

7

Relief

12th September 04: My friend Simon had suggested we go away for a week to Ireland for a break, regardless of surgery results. Of course, that was before we knew anything about my having to have a mastectomy. Regardless of this impending surgery, we decide to go to Ireland with my nine-year-old Josh and Simon's fifteen-year-old daughter, Rebecca. Funnily enough, we have a great time. I am actually able to let the prospect of mastectomy surgery fall to the back of my mind. We have booked a 'cottage', which is described as situated on 'a short walk up a steep hill'. When we arrive, the 'cottage' is actually a three bedroomed semi-detached house on a housing estate, a long walk up a slight incline. We fall about laughing. Now there are two ways of approaching this holiday: either we find a phone and tear a strip off the holiday company for misleading us and demand our money back, or we enjoy this valuable time together. A couple of years ago, I would have got very annoyed about this. Now I choose to make the most of this opportunity to have a fun time together. If Josh and I can achieve this attitude of mind prior to mastectomy surgery, then the possibilities are endless.

16th September 04: The evening before I go into hospital for surgery, I ring ahead to find out where I am on the surgeon's operating schedule. I am the surgeon's first mastectomy that morning so I agree to be admitted later this evening. At least, I will not have to go without food for too long nor will I have to wait for hours, increasing my anxiety. My friend Claire is travelling up to me this evening and seeing me into hospital later. I ring the hospital ahead to find out the latest time I can come in. One of the nurses concedes that I can come in at 9.30pm. I am delighted. I am enjoying myself, feeling like a naughty schoolgirl who is allowed to stay out longer. So when Claire arrives, we open a bottle of wine and have a great chat. Minutes later, I hear the key turning in my front door and it's my friend Angie, coming to collect a few extra things for Josh. She looks stunned seeing us laughing and drinking. I suppose this is a strange sight for anyone, prior to such major surgery. In my mind, I have tried everything else, so I am ready for this surgery. I know the routine in the hospital and I have the right friends around me. This is my decision in my own time and I am ready.

17th September 04: This morning I wake really early in hospital to see my reliable, special friend Geraldine arriving to go down to theatre with me. I asked Geraldine because she is so 'grounded and still' in herself. As I am getting ready for theatre, Geraldine repeats: 'You know Jacinta, you can do this alone. You are so much more than your body' and I now know this. However, I want her with me, just till I go to asleep. As we head off down to theatre poor Geraldine has to squeeze herself between my trolley and the ward walls. I urge her to just keep coming with me, until someone says 'No'. We reach the entrance to the pre-op room and then a nurse steps in, refusing to allow my friend in with me. This is unusual because up until then each one of my friends came into the pre-op room and stayed till I went to sleep. This time, I feel much stronger. I wave goodbye to Geraldine and am wheeled into this clinical, barren room to be prepared for surgery. I insist on seeing the consultant first before I go to sleep. He comes through from theatre and asks to have a look at my breast. He looks surprised and then I realise I am squeezing the life out of his hand. 'Please get all the Cancer for me'. I then let go, much to his relief. I am now in his and God's hands.

Several hours later, I slowly start coming round in a very dark room with black walls and a nurse dressed all in dark green sitting on either side of me. I try to get up but feel weighed down, unable to move. One of the nurses tells me that I am in the recovery room and just had surgery to remove my breast. They ask me if I would like to see where my breast had been. I cautiously look down under my gown to see I am flat on one side, completely wrapped in bandages. My instant reaction is a feeling of relief! Thank goodness, it has gone.

A few days later my friends Janet and Keith come in to see me. I feel good and happy. We start chatting and as I rabbit on: 'I lie on my right side looking out the window with the fan on the side table gently blowing in my direction. I can see the blue sky over the top of the rundown exterior buildings and I feel that I am away on a tropical island', Keith smiles and asks me how much morphine I have had. Of course I am still attached to the morphine machine – oops!!! Eventually I call the nurse to take the machine away. I am getting to like it and find that I have been using it in case I feel pain! So I think it is time for us to part company. Morphine is toxic to my system, slowing down my heart rate but killing any pain. I decide to let go of my new bedmate. Whatever pain there may have been has gone. It helped initially and for that I am very grateful.

19th September 04: This morning, several new doctors approach my bed with the Ward Sister. They stand at the end of my bed and without telling me their names, ask me how I am doing. I do wish doctors would come and actually sit down beside my bed and talk to my head, not to my feet. Anyway, before I know it, they tell me: 'We will remove your bandage and have a look at your scar'. Before I realise what I am doing, I find myself retreating up the back of my bed towards the ceiling as far away as I can get, to avoid this unexpected onslaught. Whatever happened to asking me first, out of respect if nothing else! I am terrified but somehow manage to utter: 'Just a minute. From the moment I woke up from this surgery, even in the post op room, I have looked down to where my breast used to be and have seen that it has gone. I have been doing this ever since, trying to accept that it is not there. The last thing I need is for you to whip the bandages off so that you can have a look, without any consideration for my feelings!' At which point the Ward Sister steps in and slowly removes it. The doctor apologises at long last and sits down beside my bed, explaining that he knows what he is doing. I personally do not doubt his ability or expertise. My concern is not to do with his expertise but about his manner and lack of consideration for my feelings. I do not stop having feelings because I am a patient, although I am sure that medical staff would much prefer it that way! Once the bandage is removed, (bear in mind that this is the first time that I have seen this scar) the doctor pulls his chair closer to have a good look. His nose is about 6 inches from my scar. He then comments, whilst intently focused on my scar (and it is mine, not his or the hospital's!): 'Wonderful, excellent work!' to which I reply: 'Can I just remind you that I am here as well!'

Mammy is drinking again and it's my fault. I don't know what I have done wrong this time. I can't stop crying, which makes mammy even madder: 'Get out of my bloody sight, you little brat' she roars, her bazookas aimed and ready as she slams the kitchen door firmly behind me, catching the backs of my heels, sending a shooting pain up my little legs. Outside the kitchen, at the top of the stairs, I cling on to the banisters, my sobbing, pained face pressed against the cold wood, longing for daddy to leave his office below. It's just 6 o'clock, he will be coming up soon. I can hear the office door creak open below. My heart lightens and excitement sweeps me up off my sore feet. It's daddy, it's daddy, he's coming upstairs. I can't wait… All of a sudden, the kitchen door flies open. Like a wild, raging storm, mammy emerges and standing at the top of the stairs, with bazookas pointed, she commands daddy into the war-torn kitchen. Daddy steps past me and disappears. He didn't even see me.

The Ward Sister asks if I am okay? How can I be okay with this! As she leaves to follow the doctors on their rounds, she whispers: 'Good on you, you tell them!' I cannot recall being in a more vulnerable position as an adult. Yet I still have to stand up for myself to medical staff! What about all those patients who are unable to do this, because of their fears, of authority, of reprisal, of whatever else. I cannot understand why doctors have to be so unbelievably detached in order to treat patients. Healing surely is much more than clinical treatment; it is as much about how the patient is treated. From my experience so far, I feel that my Cancer is being treated without any real concern for me as a person. The Breast Care Nurses offer support here and there, which I welcome and appreciate, but why can doctors not offer compassion and care. Luckily for me, my friend Angie appears at this moment. I cannot hold back my distress. Angie holds me in her arms and I cry from the very pit of my stomach. A moment later, a nurse peeps through the curtain saying that my son is standing out on the ward crying. Angie had asked a nurse to take him to the day room but obviously Josh heard me crying. It breaks my heart to see my boy so distressed. I call him in. We just clutch each other and cry together. After a while, Angie leaves us alone. Josh and I always talk through every stage of our journey and somehow we seem to get by. God knows how, or perhaps that's just it – God knows and is there for us. One of the nurses later tells me that she feels that it was good for Josh to have been able to share my upset. It gave him an opportunity to break down also. God, this is so hard at times, but tremendously healing.

21st September 04: Once I start to feel well, a few days after my mastectomy, I happen to mention that I am thinking about going home. Before I know it, my drains are removed and I am moved to a larger ward. I imagine that the nurses need my bed for another patient. Unfortunately this time I feel too weary to express my reluctance to move, as I feel comfortable and secure here. I am lucky I am not out in the corridor!

I find it difficult adjusting to a different ward. After my mastectomy, the slightest thing can really be upsetting. I feel a bit lost. I do not know anyone around me. I have been doing so well up to this point. This quick and sudden change of ward is the last thing I need and throws me into despair. I do not want to see or talk to anyone. I feel miserable. However, a few hours later I start to pick up again. I happen to overhear the patient in the bed next to me expressing how anxious and frightened she feels about her imminent mastectomy and lymph node removal surgery later that day. This is a large-breasted lady who has had only two weeks to absorb the shock of diagnosis, understand what is happening to her and prepare for surgery. I feel lucky in comparison. I have had six months and three surgeries to prepare for my mastectomy and I needed every minute of this time to come to terms with what was happening to me. How is this poor lady going to cope with all of this?

One of the Breast Cancer Consultants comes in to see me prior to my leaving later that day. In his usual detached, distant manner, he comments on the small swelling around my scar. He suggests that he could drain this fluid off with a needle in clinic afterwards! Realising that I am not happy with this, he tries to ease my concern by telling me that he does this all the time. Why do health staff say this? How can this information ease my fear? Instead I feel patronised. I do not doubt his ability. All I really want is for him to understand how frightened I feel. His subsequent behaviour with the 'terrified' patient next to me confirms my worst fears. I cannot help but wonder how this consultant would feel if our positions were reversed. I am sure that he would feel just the same if I suggested draining the fluid off the swelling on his remaining testicle! The consultant leaves the ward. My frightened neighbour is now in a state of panic. I ask if I can help. She had no idea prior to seeing this consultant that she would have to have hormone treatment, chemotherapy and radiotherapy after surgery and, on top of that, travel to Oxford. This poor lady is beside herself. Does she really need to know this additional information just before going down to theatre for a mastectomy? Where is the sensitivity, the compassion and, heaven helps us, the empathy?

I understand exactly how she feels. I suggest she talks to the Breast Care Nurse about how she is feeling, so that she can approach her surgery in a better frame of mind. She seems calmer after sharing her feelings. Clutching at straws to lift her spirits, I show her my little brochure of breast lingerie and there are some lovely mastectomy bras especially for larger ladies. She is surprised. Actually so am I, as I have only seen this brochure earlier today.

22nd September 04: Today I am due to leave hospital (five days after my mastectomy). The Breast Care Nurse beckons me to come into the bathroom. She promptly pulls out what looks like a piece of sponge, suggesting that I wear this inside my bra so that I can appear 'normal!' when leaving the hospital. I know she is trying to help but I know that my breast has been cut off. Nothing will change that for me. Why do others assume that what matters most to patients with Breast Cancer, having had a mastectomy, is to appear the same as they were before they had their breast removed (as if this fixes everything!)? How I look does not matter to me at the moment but how I feel does. I can stick whatever you like in the place of my 'missing breast', whether it be a sponge, prosthesis or reconstructed breast, but I personally need to come to terms with my 'loss' before I even begin to consider plastering over it.

On leaving the hospital with only one breast, I suggest to my friend Simon that we go to Hartwell for a drink. I like to celebrate every step of this bumpy road. Simon looks shocked. I cannot quite manage a glass' of wine but I do manage tea and sandwiches. Yippee, I am out and even more of me is alive this time! Less is certainly more in my case.

29th September 04: Now, just a week after coming home, Simon needs to go back home to Liverpool. I feel panicky. How am I going to manage? I feel so tired, weepy and sore after the surgery. Then another angel comes into our lives: my friend Sue in Wales, recovering from Breast Cancer some five years earlier, invites Josh and I down to her home for the following week. I feel so relieved.

2nd October 04: As I slowly wake up this morning, I feel anxious and jumpy inside. I am having all my stitches removed today and not looking forward to it. Later we are travelling down to Wales – quite a lot for one day! I ask Simon to stay with me while the nurse removes my stitches. Poor man, he tries subtly to get out of this by suggesting that my neighbour may be more helpful. However much as I understand his reluctance, I need him to be there for me. This is quite a request as Simon is an ex-boyfriend, as well as a good friend. Ten minutes before the district nurse is due to call, I go upstairs to my bedroom and prepare myself for this ordeal. First I have to prepare Simon for what he is about to see, and that is not easy. The district nurse arrives, comes upstairs and sits beside my bed. Simon and I clutch hands nervously, holding on to each other for dear life. I am not sure who is supporting whom. I am definitely not going to let Simon out of this room, no matter what happens, and I think he knows it. Once the first couple of an endless row of stitches are removed, I am relieved that it didn't really hurt, so much so that I start relating the story of the patient I met at my advisory day who had had a reconstruction and was waiting for the nipple to arrive later. Then Simon and I both roar with laughter, my whole body shakes and the poor nurse struggles to focus on my moving flat chest. Black comedy to say the least!

Later in the afternoon, Simon drives Josh and I down to Wales. This week, staying with our friends Sue, Roger, their son Joseph and Bonnie their dog, gives us both precious time to heal within the loving support of a close family.

I even manage to have a shower and start looking at my massive scar. Of course, this will take a long time to sink in. My breast has gone and so has my tumour. I tried my best to hold on to it, my breast that is. I think that taking my time having this surgery has helped me cope with the loss better. As the Ward Sister said at the time, 'You seem to have been grieving a little after each surgery which is probably helping you now.' My instant feeling of relief after surgery is helping me heal quicker psychologically. I even start walking around the quiet lanes near Sue's home. One particular day I ask Josh if he wants to come out with me but he declines. I call Bonnie and off we go together. Josh's face is a picture: 'But mum, you are afraid of dogs!' I am not just afraid of dogs, I am beyond terrified. Dogs have something to do with abuse for me. But today is very different. I don't feel afraid.

'Dogs don't bother me today, Josh'. I feel very happy. Josh and I are recovering together. We are loved. I can handle looking at myself without my breast. That's a good start. I feel good in myself, which is amazing. I guess I am stronger than I think.

A beautiful Sunday afternoon on the beach in Buncrana, County Donegal. Mammy and daddy entrenched in their usual corner, with the rocks nearby providing shelter from the fine sand whipping across the desolated beach. Deirdre, Gerard and I are happy playing in and out of the water. Suddenly everything changes. A huge black dog, breathing heavily, drools warm, pungent saliva onto my tiny, frozen face. Caught between the vice-like grip of this massive black beast, pinning my small, quivering body down on the sodden sand, and the giant waves creeping up on my mounting terror, I cannot move. I scream but no sound emanates from my stiff body. A chaotic blend of white light and flashing stars jerks me up into the air. Shaking, sobbing, soaking wet, I run desperately to catch up with mammy and daddy. They are walking along the beach shouting at each other. I feel so shaken, frightened and abandoned all at the same time. They cannot see me. They cannot hear me.

9th October 04: Today Sue and her husband Roger drive us back to Bristol, where my lovely neighbour Silvia meets us to bring us home. Aren't we the lucky ones! My family of friends are there for us when it really matters. We are so grateful. We will never forget their amazing unconditional love and support when all the chips were down. With good friends, you can get through

Cancer as a single mother even without family support. What's more, there are no hidden agendas or senses of obligation.

I remember that when I gave birth to Josh in 1995 my anticipation of the event was terrifying. Yet when I was actually giving birth, it really was not so bad at all. After I had given birth, I was completely amazed and over the moon. I had faced a fear and come through it. What a gift! This experience is similar to how I have coped with my treatment so far: before each surgery, I was gripped with fear and horror, believing that I might not wake up again. I actually wrote out a will before my operations and had my closest friends witness it. I was so convinced that I would not survive. Then, as I woke up again not in pain, I was thrilled. This actually sustained me through a nightmare of recurrent surgeries, post-op recovery and poor results. Each time I overcame my fear, my spirits lifted and I was so proud of myself and felt more 'at peace' inside. I remember my words to my Breast Cancer Consultant after my third operation: 'Its like this, really – each time you cut out a piece of my physical body, I gain an internal spiritual part of me'. As I face fear each time through surgery, I emerge stronger, recovering more of me that has lain dormant, suppressed by years of fear. Imagine how my patient file reads!

19th October 04: Today is the court hearing for my driving offence and possible ban. Martin comes with me to court in Oxford, thankfully. I have never been into court before. Upon hearing my name called, I walk into court, immediately feeling dwarfed by the three-tiered structure in front of me. Three judges and two clerks peer down at me. I feel shaky. I begin to relate my story, holding on to the table before me for dear life. Believe me, if there is any question of my being in denial of my Cancer, this experience certainly blasts it out of the water. After what seems likes hours, one of the judges surprisingly asks me if I would like a glass of water to which I agree. The judges then disappear from the courtroom for what seems like an eternity. When they reappear, I am asked to stand. Then the dreaded words are spoken: 'after due consideration of your circumstances, we have decided to ban you for three…' Oh no, not a ban for three months or years, how can I manage?'

Then another judge seems to shout: 'Have you heard what we said?' I don't think I did. By this stage, my fingers have turned white. He then repeats: 'You are banned for three days'. What! I cannot believe what I have just heard. 'Are you sure?' I ask dubiously. His face slowly reveals a reassuring smile as he nods to me. I finally let go of the table and breathe. Phew that was too close!

My tummy starts jumping inside, my little hands clutching my dress, my heart banging inside my chest. Mammy is drinking from her secret tea again and her eyes are getting darker and darker as she stares at me. Unable to stop shaking, I dash upstairs as mammy blows up at daddy, locking myself in the bathroom – a long plain, greenish room with a bath, sink and single window. There I sit on the small window ledge unable to move in case I make the fighting worse. I want to disappear. Eventually daddy comes and encourages me to come out, telling me that everything is okay, even when I know it can never be okay. He is lying, but I believe him. I want to believe him so much. I would love a cuddle but he never holds me anymore. I don't know why. What have I done wrong? I just don't understand.

8

Squidgy

6th November 04: My friend Auriel comes with me for this special event. We are guided to a different part of the hospital and shown into a warm cosy room – the first I have seen. How nice. I would like to have been in this room when I was initially diagnosed. The comfortable surroundings would have helped ease the blow a little. Every little helps. It feels strange trying on different prostheses. I am still too shell-shocked from my diagnosis and four surgeries to really consider which prosthesis I need. Fortunately, I am very small, so the smallest one fits me fine. I need time to become familiar with this object and get to know 'it', as it were, before I can start wearing it and accepting it as part of my body and my new life now. So I bring my new friend home.

Now it is time to introduce my new friend to Josh. Gosh how do I do that? Well I guess I just get on with it. There is nothing to be gained from avoiding this. The beauty with children is that they just accept things as they are – a quality that we lose sometimes as adults. I arrive back home just before Josh gets back from school. After a little while, I call Josh upstairs. As he bundles into my bedroom, he quickly notices the box on my bed. I explain that I have been back to the hospital to receive my present of a new breast. We open the box together anticipating its contents. Josh picks it up and feeling it, he pulls a face, saying: 'It's Squidgy', so my new breast is now christened 'Squidgy' and officially joins our family. Josh simply accepts our new friend.

I rush out of the kitchen and hide in the pantry, as mum calls it. This dim, long room is as big as our bathroom upstairs. On the same floor as our lived-in, 'fighting' kitchen and opposite the posh drawing room, bare surface tops with shelves upon shelves containing jars and jars of mum's inept jam-making attempts stretch deep on either side above musty, mostly empty cupboards. A single window at the far end overlooking Castle Street provides a hint of daylight. Here I crawl into one of the many dark, vacuous cupboards and remain absolutely still, barely daring to breathe. Hours pass by and no one comes for me. Tentatively I crawl out of the cupboard and slowly open the pantry door. I tiptoe across the landing to the kitchen and listen quietly at the door. Not a sound. I peep through the key-hole – daddy is sitting in his favourite armchair looking terrible, mammy is drinking in silence. I can't see Deirdre or Gerard. Maybe they are upstairs somewhere. I don't know what is really happening. I don't feel safe so run upstairs to my bedroom and hide under the bed clothes.

9th November 04: Now it is time to see the oncologist for the first time. My friend Auriel comes with me. I understand that I will be seeing the male senior oncologist but when we are called in, I discover that it is a lady instead. I am still trying to come to terms with my mastectomy and wearing my prosthesis. My poor body is still recovering from four general aesthetics in four months. As we listen to this oncologist talk about follow-on treatment including: hormone treatment followed by chemotherapy and then radiotherapy, I am in a daze. What does all this mean? How can I decide what to do when I do not understand how these treatments work, their side effects in the short and long terms. When I ask about my chances with chemotherapy, I am astounded to hear that chemotherapy will only reduce my chances of a recurrence by 3%, as my Cancer is not in my lymph nodes. I want to think about radiotherapy and chemotherapy but my gut instinct says 'no' to chemotherapy. What about my immune system? The shock of diagnosis followed by four general anaesthetics and surgical procedures in four months has already taken a high toll on my body and my already depleted immune system. I do not want to risk a medley of toxic drugs flowing through my veins with such poor chances of effectiveness. I am not convinced about radiotherapy either. I agree to have Tamoxifen – a hormone blocker. Auriel and I leave this appointment feeling battered and confused. What an enormous amount of information to absorb in one meeting. This is impossible. How can I possibly decide? I need to know so much more, I am not convinced about this course of treatment. I get the distinct impression that the oncologist expects me to decide here and now. I feel like one of many patients being put through the system as quickly as possible. I would have preferred to have heard information about each follow-up treatment in separate meetings: once, for example, as to hormone treatment, with ample opportunity to discuss the benefits, side effects, long-term effects, before deciding. If I agree to all three types of follow-on treatment now being offered, my decision will be based on fear. I need time to learn more about these treatments, so that I can make an informed, well-considered choice.

1st December 04: Now I have to find a new bra for my prosthesis. I do not know where to look, how to ask for it. All seemingly minor concerns, yet very important ones. First of all, I pick up some catalogues from the Breast Care Nurses at the hospital. Next I ring up some shops. Then I muster some courage and walk into a major High Street store, self-consciously asking the assistant in lingerie if she has some mastectomy bras in stock. She replies by saying: 'No' and that was that. Her abrupt manner leaves me feeling more vulnerable and embarrassed. This experience is a really important step for me. My friend Auriel kindly offers to take me to some shops to try special bras on. Poor Auriel, little does she realise where her offer might take her! I eventually contact Amoena who are very helpful. They offer a special service whereby you can come to their showroom in Southampton and spend up to two hours with a specially trained assistant trying on lots of bras. This sounds much better – Amoena staff come across as competent and understanding of the needs of customers with breast surgery. So off we go to Southampton. This is the best thing I ever did. I feel quite nervous entering this building, which looks like a factory outlet. We are warmly greeted by a friendly face that shows us into their showroom – quite a large room with racks of swimming costumes and bras as well as a curtained changing cubicle. I aim for the cubicle where I fully undress. The first tentative stage for me is letting the assistant see my scar. Once I see that she accepts my scar without flinching, I feel relieved and a little more relaxed.

It is hard to imagine just how much of a hurdle each step through Cancer really is and there are hurdles where you least expect them. I start trying on several pocketed bras, having inserted my prosthesis into the pocket within each bra – this procedure in itself is all completely new to me and does not come to me easily. In fact I feel quite awkward at first, almost like when I was initially learning to ski – a strange analogy, I know, but even putting on your ski boots for the first time is quite an achievement in itself! This is no different. The bras do not really fit very well and I start to get disheartened. Then my friend Auriel chooses some more bras for me and encourages me to try a few more. Having tried about another five, I find one that suits me. I start to get excited – feeling good about my appearance. Then I find another bra that feels really good. What an amazing boost to my self-confidence. Then Auriel mentions the swimsuits on a rack out in the showroom, so I tentatively try on some swimsuits. Guess what I end up doing as my confidence grows? Prancing about the showroom in only my skimpy knickers, trying on different costumes. Gosh I feel good in my own skin! In the end I choose two bras (one black and one white) and two swimming costumes. My friend buys a swimming costume, too, and she has both her breasts!

I leave that showroom having reached a state of self-confidence that I find hard to believe, and only ten weeks after my mastectomy. This visit to Amoena was well worth every mile and minute. It has been a terrific day out. Who would have thought that a day trip to a catalogue outlet could restore my confidence in my body and in myself to such an extent? I am so grateful to my friend Auriel who came with me. She does not know how much she helped me. This experience has been so important to my physical and mental healing process. It is so important to go with gut feeling in these matters rather than rationalising the event, which in this case would probably have ended up with my ordering from their catalogue to save time, effort and petrol.

Christmas morning, we all rush downstairs to the living room and there under the big mahogany dining table lie our presents in three neat piles. Daddy mentions that there is a special present for me downstairs in the back yard. I gallop down the stairs to the hall below and run out the back door. There standing in front of me is my very own little house. Daddy put it up for me the night before. It has two little front windows, a side window and a back window. It is made of plastic but I can see through the windows and I can stand up inside. This is my place. I spend all Christmas day in my own house – my special Christmas present that daddy made just for me. Here I can hear the rain pelting down on the plastic roof and it sounds great. Everything is okay in my own wee house.

9

Touching Peace

2005

3rd-5th February 05: I have wanted to go to a retreat ever since I came out of hospital the first time. Now, four operations later, I definitely want to do something about it. So I start searching the internet. I don't really want a physically demanding retreat nor do I want a retreat with a particular religious bias. I find: Brahma Kumaris Global Retreat Centre at Nuneham Courtney just outside Oxford. I glance at their website and am grabbed by the following description of the retreat Centre:

'Since 1993, the Global Retreat Centre at Nuneham House (administered by the Brahma Kumaris World Spiritual University UK) has welcomed thousands of people from across the world. They come to restore balance and focus to their lives through solitude, silence and the study of spiritual values. Tucked away in the rolling countryside of Oxfordshire, surrounded by fifty-five acres of historical gardens and overlooking the River Thames, Nuneham Park is the perfect location to step away from the frantic pace of modern living, and to rediscover your inner peace and power.'

The phrase 'Tucked away' appeals to me. It sounds womb-like and nurturing and I know somehow that I need lots of that. The last phrase leaps off the web page at me: 'Rediscover your inner peace and power' especially 'power'. As a little child, daddy took away my personal power. Now as an adult dealing with Cancer, I feel powerless all over again. But I am determined to change this. The description of the retreat itself sounds right up my street:

'A weekend meditation retreat at the Global Retreat Centre provides guidance in meditation and the development of spiritual wisdom. Sessions are led by experienced members of the Brahma Kumaris University. In between sessions, there is time to rest, relax and explore the beautiful grounds at Nuneham Park that overlook the River Thames, with areas for solitude, personal study and walks … and the riverside is an ideal place for reflection.

The Retreat Centre also offers guests the opportunity to stay in a pure, serene and spiritual environment, where vegetarian diet and abstinence from alcohol and cigarettes is observed. Accommodation is provided in twin bedrooms with en-suite bathrooms.'

Right now this sounds like heaven to me and, more importantly, it simply feels right. I don't need to know much more. I ring up and ask about fees for a residential retreat but a sweet voice replies: 'You will know what to give while you are here'. That's good enough for me. I complete their simple booking form on line. I just need to make sure that Josh is happy while I am away for a couple of days. My booking is confirmed and I am off – two whole days in a beautiful retreat centre all for 'spiritual' little me. It may sound strange but when confronted by the unknown in relation to my physical life on this planet, I fall apart and struggle to cope yet when dealing with my spiritual life, I welcome the unexpected. Somehow, I know that I will not be disappointed, only enlightened. Perhaps this is where I can learn to 'trust'.

I have no idea what to expect as I drive in through the gated entrance and long driveway to this imposing building, nestled within beautiful grounds. I am welcomed by a lady dressed all in white who gives me a sticky label bearing my name. As more people arrive, we are shown up a grand, winding staircase to our bedrooms and then invited to meet up in the meditation room on the first floor. My bedroom is spacious with two beds, well decorated, with stunning views over the well-kept grounds. After settling in, I make my way to the meditation room and add my shoes to the numerous pairs of different shapes, colours and sizes neatly placed just outside the door. As I enter, rows and rows of people sit facing a small platform. I quietly settle into an empty chair. Another lady dressed in white with a warm, radiant smile serenely occupies the stage. I feel a strange sense of excitement.

I am amazed to hear that everyone who works here, although 'work' does not seem like the appropriate word, does voluntarily, mostly as part of the Brahma Kumaris community.[2] This impressive establishment is funded purely by donations. This explains the atmosphere of peace and love that pervades this wonderful place. I feel that my soul is being fed in many ways here, through the meditation sessions, lectures and talks on different aspects of spirituality, home-cooked, wholesome vegetarian meals lovingly prepared and peaceful walks in silence within the well-tended grounds. I feel love everywhere.

As I climb into bed this same evening feeling nicely tired, the door bursts open and a lady enters. She explains that she is staying in my room as she is also on retreat. I had no idea I was sharing but then there are two beds. I say 'hello' then 'goodnight' and drop off to sleep with no concern whatsoever.

Later the following day, my room mate and I start chatting and asking each other why we decided to come here. She surprises me by explaining that she is a barrister in London with one of the big law firms but came here to consider her current relationship and her deep desire to change to a career as a yoga class teacher. Quite a career-change, but I imagine more fulfilling in many ways. I admire her courage.

We are introduced to Meditation gently. 'The basic understanding in Raja Yoga meditation, which the university teaches, is that each one of us is an eternal spirit or soul. Like actors taking on a costume, we express ourselves on the 'stage' of the world through our physical bodies. As souls, our original nature is filled with the highest qualities of peace, purity, love, joy and power. However, over time, forgetting this spiritual truth, we have lost ourselves in an addictive search for temporary

---

[2] See Appendix B for more information on the global retreat and the Brahma Kumaris community and their retreats, talks and courses at the end of this book.

happiness through physical and material means. This has brought us into a state of worry, fear and conflict.'

According to their website, some members within the BK community prefer to wear white, as it reflects inner aspirations towards living a life of simplicity, purity, cleanliness and truth – qualities to which the practice of Raja Yoga meditation gives rise. This lady simply sits with her back straight, hands relaxed across her lap and, oddest of all, her eyes open. I understand that here meditation is always done with eyes open to avoid falling asleep. Personally I prefer to close my eyes. Then all kinds of thoughts race through my head but, with practice and longer periods, these thoughts subside and I lose myself. It is hard to explain this, but I love losing myself in this way because, in doing so, I seem to find myself. It is as though I leave my body for a while and become spirit or soul, as BKs believe. Every member of the BK community begins and ends their talks with the phrase: 'Ohm Shanti' which means 'I am soul'. At the end of this meditation I feel peace and a warm sense of belonging.

The following day, as I arrive and join everyone for a longer meditation, a middle-aged lady beside me, whom I don't know, promptly declares: 'I am going to leave my husband'. She goes on to explain that this is the first time that she has actually voiced her decision. Gosh!

The following morning, I join everyone for a further half hour meditation, during which I experience such incredible beauty deep inside me, bringing tears to my eyes. I feel that I have found a little more of me, more to hold on to. I feel loved. I get the impression that many of us come here searching for something, stepping out of day-to-day living to find it within ourselves. It is almost as if, by taking this time out, we are able to get in touch with our 'Soul' or 'God' selves.

This weekend has given me cherished time to find the courage to stop and listen to my inner self in the midst of my nightmare. I leave this centre at the end of my weekend enveloped in love, safe and secure with a renewed strength and determination. I feel peaceful and whole. Before leaving, I purchase a CD from the bookshop entitled 'Understanding

Karma' to help me at home. I particularly like this wonderful track: 'A Meditation on Freedom'. I find the words very moving:

'I sit quietly and look into the mirror of my own mind. I see the eternal being – the soul. In the presence of God, I can see the huge amount of karma that I have accumulated. I have continued to add to my burden from one birth to the next and now, in the presence of God, I begin to experience God's love, God's mercy. My eternal mother is coming to set me free. My eternal mother is taking responsibility. I simply have to hand over. I simply have to let go. My mother gives me a signal that if I let go, I can be free. I need not carry this burden anymore. If I choose, I can let go of the past, of my weaknesses, of my limits and, in this new awareness of being a child of God, claim freedom as my birthright. With the power of love, my mother and my father set me free. They show me the way to fly so that I transcend all the obstacles and difficulties that I created for myself. I can fly and attain my original state of perfection. In the presence of God's mercy and love, I am free.'

I can play this track and meditate and hopefully won't feel so alone.

10

A Rock in the Storm

10th February 05: Looking on the Internet for a wholistic doctor, I find Dr. Rosy Daniel of Health Creation. I also recall seeing her interviewed on TV regarding the indian ayurvedic herbal remedy Carctol. I make an appointment to see her in Bristol with my friend Martin. I am so keen to find out all I can about my dis-ease from a wholistic point of view.

We drive down and arrive at her office in good time. I feel vulnerable, confused and anxious to find some answers. We both sit in her waiting room. I eagerly start sifting through the entire reading material available on all sorts of complementary treatment, desperate to find some answers. Perhaps if I can find some answers here then I can regain some control in my life.

We are shown into Rosy's office and are introduced. Dr. Rosy Daniel immediately strikes me as a very compassionate, warm and knowledgeable lady. I am aware that she does not have access to my medical files so is relying on my explanation of my Cancer diagnosis and current treatment. She is interested in me not just my dis-ease. After so much surgery and clinical, dispassionate treatment up to now, I feel almost neutralised as a person. Rosy's warmth is a welcome relief. It is important to me that Rosy is medically qualified as well as having vast knowledge of complementary medicine. I am really looking for a wholistic approach to Cancer not an alternative.

Rosy explains Cancer to me in a way that gives me a wholistic overview. For the first time, this makes sense and I can see how I need to be treated mentally, physically and spiritually in order to heal properly. I find this very helpful in that it helps me to help myself. [3]

---

[3] You can find Rosy's Recommendations in full at Appendix C at the end of this book.

My visit to Rosy influences my approach to my dis-ease, helping me feel less a victim. I would like to continue seeing Rosy as a patient but distance is prohibitive. I decide to keep in touch by telephone every few months, as I need to. Here I have found one valuable source of wholistic support in my raging storm.

As we are all going to bed, mammy and daddy's socialising world takes off in the posh drawing room. I sneak out of bed and peering through one of the wooden banisters at the top of the stairs, I can see people dressed in some sort of uniform bringing in plates and plates of lovely food, mammy dressed in her finest clothes and daddy coming up from the office downstairs. I can hear everyone arrive, then chatting and drinking as mammy sings and plays the piano. She loves dressing up and putting on a big show. I don't think Daddy loves it so much. He just seems to do what mammy says. As it gets later, mammy and her friends get louder and louder as they drink more and more. Then I hear shouting and swearing. Mammy is swearing at her friends and daddy is trying to stop it. In the end mammy's friends storm out and then mammy starts on daddy. I do wish he would get us all some help.

7th May 05: Having noticed a further little lump along my mastectomy scarline, the consultant suggests that I have it removed in day surgery. As this prospect of even more surgery gradually sinks in, my anxiety steadily increases. I telephone the day surgery unit and ask to speak to the Ward Sister, Jackie Benson. I know that Nick Bigwood, the Patient Advice and Liaison Service manager, has intervened and requested a general anaesthetic for me, as opposed to a local. I voice my concerns regarding which type of anaesthetic I will be given, as I do not want to be sent into orbit: sedated – yes, orbit – no! For the first time, this lady hears not just my words but my underlying fear and anxiety about yet another procedure within 12 months. She gently comments that I sound anxious and asks if I would like to come down to see her. I immediately phone my friend Auriel, who fortunately is free to come with me. Jackie goes through all my concerns, even to the point of finding my file and checking on the specific sedation that will be used, then confirming that the Breast Cancer Consultant will be performing the surgery himself. She reassures me that she will see me when I come in for the procedure in three days time. I feel understood and reassured. This is the first time that I have felt cared for since I was diagnosed. After our heartening conversation, I feel relieved and even, dare I say, quite relaxed about having this procedure.

10th May 05: As Auriel and I arrive for day surgery, Jackie, true to her word, is there to welcome us. After I have changed into a gown she personally takes me down to theatre in a wheelchair, with Auriel alongside. On the way, a member of staff mentions that there is a call for her and offers to take over. She declines, explaining she is busy. She even stays with me till I am asleep and she is there when I wake up again. I come through this procedure so much more easily due to this lady's care and commitment. I feel so grateful that she listened, understood, genuinely cared, and followed through on her promises. Now this is what I call excellent patient care and empowerment. Sadly it only happens rarely. I imagine that due to many factors, including lack of resources, outdated attitudes, government targets and staffing levels, this level of humane treatment cannot be a priority.

23rd May 05: Simon comes with me this time to hear the results of this surgery. We are shown into another small, plain looking room without any character, I always notice those ominous, clinical signs. First the Breast Care Nurse appears, slowly followed by 'that nurse' again. Then eventually, yet another unknown consultant emerges. How many can there be? I know the results are not good but I am more used to this than Simon. The consultant very tentatively tells me that they successfully removed the lump but it is cancerous. I ask if it is invasive and he nods. I think that both nurses expect me to get all 'anxious and emotional' again. After all, this indictment, imprinted on my file follows me wherever I go. I take one look at Simon and he has turned the whitest shade of white I have ever seen. I am so concerned about him that my own emotions never surface. The consultant suggests rather anxiously that I have radiotherapy to prevent further recurrences. I later agree to this, although reluctantly. We leave and sit outside – speechless. After this experience, I decide that Simon should not come with me any more. It is important to me in these situations that I feel able to let my emotions out without considering the needs of someone close to me.

14th June 05: After having my cyst removed, I have an appointment to see yet another oncologist. My friend Auriel comes with me, thank goodness. I am worried now about my Cancer coming back to the same area, along my mastectomy scar-line, after only one year and I have some concerns regarding radiotherapy. I have written down some questions before our meeting to make sure that I remember.

'I have been offered radiotherapy before, either five times a week or two or three times per week: what do you suggest as the better option for me?' His off-hand reply stuns me: 'Well, it is no skin off my nose which option you have, we have hundreds of patients waiting to have this treatment.' Picking myself up I continue: "Can you tell me if I am HER2 positive?' He replies: 'Oh that's not important at this stage'. This dismissive reply delays my treatment with Herceptin by ten months, as will become clear later. However he does offer me some valuable information that Tamoxifen may not be working.

I leave his office very angry. I feel that I am one amongst hundreds of patients on a conveyor-belt. I can appreciate that this consultant may have seen hundreds of patients that day and may have had to give some patients very bad news and he may be over-tired. But however stressed and pressurised this consultant may be, he is not facing his own mortality and this does not excuse his appalling manner, devoid of care and compassion. After this upsetting experience, I decide to obtain a second opinion.

18th June 05: Meeting my wholistic doctor for the first time is the start of my taking control of my disease.

I believe that Cancer is my own systemic disease. I contributed to the growth of Cancer in my body through denying myself most of my life. I am sure that there have also been other influencing physical factors, including the contraceptive pill, Hormone Replacement Therapy and genetics, to name a few. But Cancer in my opinion is a disease of my whole system not just parts of my physical body. Therefore healing needs to occur an all levels, mind, body and spirit. By owning my dis-ease, I am taking responsibility for my healing and taking an active, committed part in my recovery.

As my life starts to fall apart and I let some of my many 'spinning plates' fall, a neighbour, Silvia, mentions that she has just met Mr and Mrs. Simi Khanna, who have just moved in a few houses along from me. She explains that Simi is an Indian wholistic doctor. Now I just have to explore this further. It is too close at hand to ignore. I ring Simi and make an appointment to see her. After conducting some initial tests, she explains that all my organs are under stress and suggests some treatment. Of course, at this stage, money is definitely a big bone of contention and a great source of worry for me. I cannot afford to really commit to this treatment fully. I help Simi out in her clinic a little which helps towards my treatment. Then my lovely neighbour Silvia surprisingly helps me out financially. I cannot get over her kindness. I am now able to have some complementary treatments, work for my local charity and fit this around my son, Josh's needs. Simi's influence and style of treatment inspires me, whilst giving my immune system a distinctive boost. In fact, Simi opens my eyes to the healing effects of complementary treatment. Having met Simi and read numerous testimonials from her patients, she strikes me as very accomplished and advanced in her field, being fully qualified as a medical doctor as well as holding qualifications in homeopathy, oxygen ozone therapy, clinical nutrition, bioresonance and other forms of bioenergetic medicine.[4]

---

[4] You can find Simi's profile and information on her brand of Causal Natural Medicine at Appendix D towards the end of this book.

Simi treats me with regular doses of active oxygen, photon laser, oxygen ozone therapy and some therapeutic infusions although my needle phobia makes this procedure very difficult for us both. These treatments, apart from the infusions, are non-invasive and very uplifting. In fact the whole experience of going for treatment with Simi is healing. I do feel treated as a person as opposed to a patient with a number on a conveyor belt.

Simi refers to health in the following terms:

'Health is not just an absence of illness, but the positive balance of all aspects of a person – body, mind, emotions and spirit.' She practices this belief in the personal way she treats her patients and I respond so well to this approach. She takes the time to answer all my questions and concerns. I feel that I am in good hands. As I spend some time with Simi both for treatment and helping out in her practice she is getting to know me. She subtly points out one day that I have the habit when faced with a decision to make, of agonising for a long time before making up my mind. This inner conflict is damaging to my system. It's almost like I create this internal friction subconsciously to hurt myself. Simi's comments ring bells, if not huge gongs, for me.

It's Saturday and I am eleven years old. Mammy brings me to town. I get so bored as mum does shopping all day. We go from Littlewoods to Woolworths and to the Post Office, to the tobacconists for mammy's cigarettes and daddy's tobacco and her long chat with the man behind the counter. Then I follow mammy up town to Austin's department store where we go to the café. She meets some of her friends and shows me off to them telling them how wonderful I am and they comment that I am a beautiful girl. I am happy lapping up all this praise. Why is it different when we get back home. I am not wonderful then. Mammy never says nice things about me indoors. What's wrong with me?

20th June 05: As I grew up as a child, conflict was what I knew: conflict, in a way, felt comfortable for me. So it has stayed with me. Inner peace and contentment have been strangers. Now I realise that 'agonising' is part of my dis-ease. As part of my healing, I must change old behaviours that are hurting me today.

No doctor can do it all. This is my responsibility. I know that there are parts of me needing to heal. It's as if I need to become whole. Perhaps this is subconsciously expressed in my desire to be treated as a whole person as I go through treatment. The gradual healing of 'all of me' we will culminate in The Issels Clinic in Mexico.

I continue seeing Simi for treatment intermittingly, for about a year until around September '06. Her presence in my life at this time supports me through a very rocky time of recurring Cancer, metatastic Cancer, radiotherapy, redundancy and the eventual sale of our home.

I realise at the time that it is no accident that Simi and I met. I believe that people come into our lives for different reasons. I am truly grateful. My following letter to Simi sums up how her treatment has helped me:

'Since being diagnosed with breast Cancer a year ago and undergoing four operations culminating in a mastectomy, I found it very difficult trusting the follow-on treatment offered by the NHS. I felt I was being treated as a number rather than an individual. Each time I saw yet another doctor or oncologist, I felt I was receiving yet another 'sentence' ending always with one or more of the regularly repeated phrases: 'in case there is anything there!' or 'as far as we can tell'.

When I went to see you, Dr Simi, for an initial consultation, I felt very quickly that you were interested in all of me 'not just my dis-ease'. I knew you understood and cared. At last, after twelve months that were agonising, not just in terms of endless operations and surgical procedures but also in terms of emotional turmoil, I knew that I had found someone who would help me truly 'heal' in all senses of the word. I knew you would treat my mind, body and spirit.

The treatments, understanding and care I have received from you over this time Simi, have changed my attitude, strengthened my immune system, helping me rise above my dis-ease, and have undoubtedly complemented my clinical treatment. I feel stronger and more in control of my life. Your caring attitude has given me hope. Thank you. Jacinta.

11

God's Family

The Leprechaun Café in Derry town centre is the place to be. Now fifteen years old, my best school friend Geraldine and I love to spend hours in The Lep after school, drinking the longest cup of coffee ever and eating one doughnut whilst watching the college boys fom St. Columbs College. It's amazing how long one coffee and one doughnut can last! We take it in turns to buy the tea and doughnut. This is the highlight of our school week and one we treasure. This afternoon Geraldine and I are engrossed in idle boy chatter when the owner, a stern-faced protestant, marches up to our table and, standing to his full height of over six foot and glaring down at me, he thunders: 'You girls cannot bloody stay here all afternoon. What do you think this place is? Get your bloody backsides out of here now'. As each nasty word emanates from his mouth, I stare at him, working desperately hard to keep my fear under wraps. Before I know it, my gentle friend is on her feet and shaking all over, she challenges this bully: 'Don't you dare speak to my friend like that, you have no right!' My friend has found her voice and she is more frightened than I am. I am gob smacked. No one has ever stood up for me. A warm glow lights up my darkness for a little while.

26th June 05: Earlier in April this year, at a Sunday Service at our local church a christening takes place as part of the service. This is beautifully done, as it is set in the centre of the church amongst the congregation. Out of the blue, Josh pipes up that he would like to be christened. He had not been christened as a baby. I thought I would wait and see what he might want to do himself, as he grew older. I am delighted. I always feel that in a way God is guiding us. We discuss it together with Canon Tim Higgins, who is very supportive and informative. When it comes to choosing godparents, Josh says that he would like Martin and Kiki, Simon, Angie and Ack as godparents and their sons Chris and Robert as godbrothers. This is beginning to sound like a mafia family! Canon Tim Higgins smiles and nods in agreement.

The day itself is just beautiful. All our special friends, with their children, are at the church. This is Josh's special day in which he has the main role. We have a beautiful service and a lovely get-together afterwards at our home. I am so proud of him. Now with the extended family of Jesus around us, we will grow even stronger through the rough times ahead.

A few days after Josh's christening, I decide to take him to a Christian shop to buy him his very own bible. We spend ages in the shop looking at all the different types. I didn't think there could be so many. Finally Josh chooses the one he prefers. Before paying for this, Josh quietly picks out a special present for me – a beautiful healing angel made of metal.

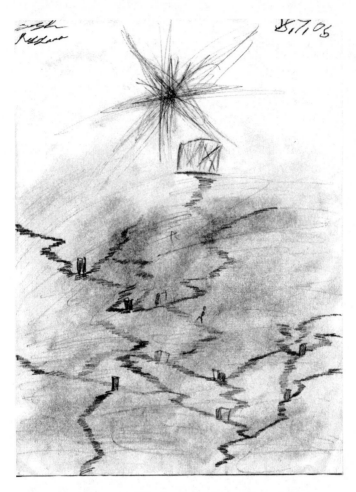

The Gated Pathway to Somewhere Nice
by Josh (8th July 05)

This sketch shows Josh's changing attitude to Cancer in our family. As I gradually heal through Cancer. I can see my growth empowering Josh.

19th July 05: As Auriel and I sit in the waiting room of The Churchill Hospital, I wonder what this new oncologist will be like. I feel bruised by my last experience and just hope that this will be better, without my having to stand up for myself again. This is all so tiring. I want to be able to form a strong relationship with my oncologist. Up to now it has been impossible as I have never met the same oncologist more than once. I only hope that fear of litigation does not join us in this meeting. My instant impression as my friend and I are shown into the consultancy room is one of respect. Upon meeting Dr. Lavery, I am struck by her attention and her considered responses. She seems to know my case. She actively listens. I am not sure, however, if she fully grasps the extent of my fear of needles, but time will tell. She does not entirely agree with my previous oncologist's suggestions. This lady comes across as humane as well as very knowledgeable. This makes a big difference. I am not necessarily looking for different medical treatment. I just want to be treated as a person and to have my faith in my treatment restored. My hope now is that, over time, this oncologist will see me as 'Jacinta' who happens to have Breast Cancer, rather than as another patient on a conveyor belt. This is exactly how it should be, but it has taken a lot of assertiveness on my part to reach this stage. Auriel and I both leave feeling more confident.

3rd August 05: This is my initial appointment to talk about my forthcoming radiotherapy sessions. I think I feel okay as I sit in the waiting room with Auriel. My friend is not allowed to come in with me but I am not letting go of her either. When I see the huge machine, I am terrified. I really do not want to have these sessions as I am concerned about the short and long-term side effects. Not a great basis for any decision.

As I strip off to my waist in front of several nurses one of whom is a male, my dignity rapidly fades into the background. I climb up on to this gigantic machine and lie there; arms outstretched while nurses manipulate my ravaged body into the right position. It has been eleven months since my mastectomy and I still feel very exposed, sore and vulnerable in this position.

Eighteen years of age and in the midst of my 'A' levels, my mind is with daddy in hospital. One unforgiving day, the dreaded call tears into my classroom. I am to go straight to the hospital. Daddy's inert body is lying in bed, as if he has already left us. Mammy is sitting by his side whispering into his ear. Fearing her premonition will come true, I stand at the end of Daddy's hospital bed gripping the bed rail with all my strength. 'Please daddy, do not suddenly sit up and scream before you leave my world'. In the whispering twilight, daddy gently and quietly slips away as if he had never been. Beside his bed: 'No Man Is an Island' written by Thomas Merton rests poignantly. My heavy shoulders let go for a moment as instant relief sweeps over me. But then a more sinister foreboding swamps my soul. My protection from mammy's lashing tongue and frantic rages has left me. I am next in line.

Daddy is gone now. I have got poor 'A' level results so decide to stay another year at school to take my 'A' levels again and to be with mammy. I want to go to Dublin University to study Spanish and Drama. Mammy refuses to take any sleeping pills. Her rages get stronger and more out of control. I listen to her for hours and hours, hearing daddy die over and over again.

Tonight at tea, mammy's mood suddenly changes again, my heart stops as I turn into myself to avoid her tirades of abuse. I sneak some of mammy's sleeping tablets and tell her I have taken four hoping that the combination of the effects of the tablets and her knowledge that I have taken them will somehow help protect me. Daddy has gone now. 'God, I wish you were here daddy: not that you ever did anything, really, but you were here and I could get out of the way'. As evening draws in, mammy is getting worse and worse, it doesn't matter what I say, she still goes on and on. I start crying and cannot stop. Now mammy is more angry grabbing my hair and pulling it as hard as she can. I cannot bear this. Her words are full of venom trying so hard to hurt me. What have I done? Perhaps I am getting what daddy used to put up with for years. I wished he had stopped her.

12

Sight of Freedom

12th August 05: Attending my first radiotherapy session is daunting, to say the least. My whole body starts shaking as I approach the huge machine. What's more, this is a different room to the one I was in before, adding to my anxiety. I do not know how I am going to distract myself when the machine starts going. One of the nurses creatively suggests that I could bring in my own music next time and they will play it for me. Now there's a thought. Thank God I spoke up. There is nothing to be gained from hiding feelings in these circumstances but it is hard to admit real fears. The next time I bring my favourite Abba music. Yes I know it is dated but I love the music and feel energised and exhilarated when I hear it. This time, I feel less anxious going in for my session. I give the nurse my CD, asking her to turn up the volume really high. There are a few raised eyebrows, as you can imagine. This is great. I cannot hear anything else. In fact the nurses have to tell me to stop moving because my little toes are dancing to the music. I dance in my mind instead. As I leave, my friend Auriel tells me that the other patients were tapping their feet to the music and smiling. How easy it is to lift a person's mood and what a simple gesture – simply bringing in your own music. This does not involve additional healthcare resources, just a little understanding and imagination!

Saturday again. Mammy, my sister and I are off to a big hotel in the seaside town, Portrush. We have packed all we need for the competitions: Miss Portrush, Miss Elegance and the Talent Competition. I really want to win the talent competition. Mammy wants me to win the other two. I feel strange getting into my swimsuit, and nothing else, to walk out on stage. All the other girls seem so much older and taller, with long brown legs and thickly made-up faces. Their hair is huge too and everybody stinks of strong perfume. I guess I look okay. Mammy says I look lovely but I don't feel right. I don't win this heat. Mammy is disappointed. I don't mind. Now it's on to the following week when I do the next heat all over again. Mammy enjoys this much more than I do.

13th August 05: Not surprisingly, Josh is beginning to exhibit difficult behaviour at school. I am in close contact with his teachers. Josh has started telling me about fights he is having at school, which is not like him at all. Some of the lovely staff from his After-School Club, Kidz @Play, describe Josh's behaviour in the playground one day after school. Josh later explains to me what happened: 'A particular boy was having a small fight with another boy. This boy dropped his hat which I picked up but this boy came up to me shouting: 'if you put my hat in the bin I will batter you'. I then dropped the hat. The boy started running at me. I defended myself although I can't remember hitting him. He then walked off, but without his hat'

The next competition later today is Miss Elegance. I am wearing one of mammy's posh long dresses and I am all made-up. I have to walk across the stage very straight and smile, even though I don't want to. I feel restricted. The dress is too tight. Mammy says that makes me look better. It's my turn. I take a big breath in and slowly tiptoe across the stage, holding in my breath, with a slight smile stuck on my heavily made-up, young face. I have made it to the other side. I gasp for air and flop. Next thing I hear is my name being called out – I have won this heat. This is the seventh heat I have entered. The judge presents me with a medal and comments: 'I have to give you points for trying'. Mammy will be pleased.

Josh is clearly struggling and probably feeling powerless at the moment. It's no wonder really, as I feel so vulnerable and groundless and I am struggling to find reassurance for Josh. I contact Mrs. Crane, the headmistress of his school, to meet with Josh and I to discuss what happened and what we can do. Surprisingly, Josh acknowledges that he is having trouble with his anger and is worried about me. I am so glad and proud that he is able to admit it: 'It made me really annoyed and I kept losing my temper. I kept getting into trouble at school cos I kept having fights with everyone' Josh.

Mrs Crane mentions The Child and Adolescent Mental Health Service for Art Therapy (CAMHS) as a possible source of support for both of us during this time. It is worth a shot, as we need all the help we can get. Consequently, I ask for a referral through our local doctor. Up to this point our wonderful friends have helped us separately, one looking after Josh while another friend takes me into hospital for surgery, hospital for treatment, follow-up appointments with doctors, and on and on. My wonderful friend Simon has been amazing, coming down from Liverpool to look after me at home after surgery. He shared our home with us for these periods, which has been very helpful. The really hard part has been at the end of the day: when we close our front door Josh and I are completely alone for the most part with Cancer – our uninvited guest. As I lie in bed alone at night, I just hope and pray that nothing happens to me suddenly in the middle of the night, because all will fall on Josh's little shoulders.

The following morning, it's my turn to do the talent competition. I am singing 'Second Hand Rose'. I feel so excited. I love singing and so much want to win this competition. I have dressed up to look the part and energetically come on stage. My nerves get the better of me and, try as I might, I can't manage to stay in tune. I am so disappointed. I have tried so many times and just can't manage to get through to the next round. I feel so useless. Mammy is not interested in this competition.

A few weeks have gone by and now it's the final of the Miss Elegance Competition. Mammy is very excited and fusses about telling me how to walk and smile and so on. I am wearing her very expensive black velvet ball gown with a small trail at the back. I am even wearing her long black gloves up to my armpits. My hair is piled high above my head, highlighting mammy's diamante drop earrings. I suppose I look great. I keep forgetting to smile. Having paraded across the stage to a packed hall, I wait in the wings with the other girls.

Our first appointment comes through for 19th August with Jan Chaundy, The Family Therapist. I have asked my friend

Martin, Josh's Godfather, to come with us to our first meeting with Jan, knowing that his presence will reassure Josh. I feel a little wary about this first meeting as I am not sure what to expect but at the same time, I know it is worth exploring. However, I quickly feel relieved once our meeting gets underway. I feel as if Jan is coming 'inside' our family to help us, as opposed to helping us from the 'outside'. I don't feel so alone with this massive burden on my weak shoulders.

The final of the Talent Competition is underway. Sadly I am not part of this much livelier competition. I can see all the different entries – some wonderful singers, so much better than me, comedians, ventriloquists and then a flamboyant bundle of energy takes over the stage, waving long, jewelled arms in the air, skimpily clad, gyrating rhythmically to the pulsating music, legs kicking powerfully into the tense atmosphere. This girl cavorts proudly down the centre of the catwalk to the delight and amazement of an unexpected audience, locked in her own world and loving every minute. Watching quietly from the wings, trussed up in my stiff costume, my heart lifts for a moment and escapes.

Time for the results, the girl beside me comes third. Then I hear my name announced in second place – gosh I have won. I walk on, relieved to collect my prize of £25 cash. I am thrilled. Mammy is not pleased and says that I should have come first. She thinks the competition is fixed and starts kicking up a fuss. My initial excitement quickly dissipates, hammering home that I am not good enough. When will I ever be good enough?

19th August 05: I look over at my wee boy who needs time and lots of support. My good friend Ange recently mentioned to me how Josh's shoulders were becoming more hunched over, day by day almost as if everything was too much for such a young child to bear. Something had to give. Josh's fight in the school playground was a cry for help and thank God, it was heard. As a result of our meeting, we discuss Josh coming to see Jonathan Isserow, the Art Therapist to help him work through his concerns using art as the focus. Josh is happy with this and will start sessions in a few weeks time. Our meeting with Jan gives us both a feeling of support 'inside' our family.

I recall looking for a book to take with me on a holiday in my early twenties, a typical romantic Danielle Steele novel. Then 'An Evil Cradling' leaps off the bookshelf at me. Without knowing what it is about, I buy it. I cannot put this book down. My friend remarks that this is quite a world away from the romantic novels I am used to and she is right. This is Brian Keenan's story of his imprisonment with John McCarthy as a hostage for five years in Beirut in 1986. He narrates his experience with humour, intelligence and great spirit. He speaks of the importance of his relationship with John in his cell and deliberately challenges the guards, all the while keeping his sense of self and spirit. He knows that no matter how much the guards beat and torture their bodies, they can do little to break their spirit. I feel jealous of Brian's Keenan's experience then. He was not alone in his cell, he had great company and most importantly, he had 'himself'. He knew who he was.

September 05-October 06: Josh has a total of approximately eighteen one-hour sessions with Jonathan during this period. Josh and I come along to the centre together and I wait downstairs while Josh goes upstairs with Jonathan. Josh appears to relate really well to Jonathon. I can see the difference in Josh as the sessions progress. He appears taller and happier. Josh does not share much with me about his sessions. I resist my urge to pry. This is Josh's special time just for him without mummy's Cancer there too. I feel that my Cancer diagnosis has taken me away from Josh as a support for a while. I know Josh needs this safe space. Towards the end of these sessions, Jonathan and I meet to discuss Josh's progress. Nothing prepares me for what he tells me. Referring to Josh's work with clay and his art portfolio, Jonathan explains that Josh is one of the most sophisticated artists of his age that he has met in terms of his skills, ability and mental approach. I am utterly amazed. Up to this point, I have only associated art therapy with therapy and have been glad of the support. I have not really considered the 'art' element much at all. No wonder these sessions are working so well – the healing blend of Jonathan's skills as a therapist, Josh's personal one-to-one time and the opportunity to work with clay. By the end of the sessions, Josh brings home all the clay models that he has made – a horse, a curved dagger, little people, other bits and pieces. Josh tells me that he chose what models to make and Jonathon helped him make them, especially strengthening the dagger. I imagine that the dagger is an uneasy mix of Cancer and anger – I recall Josh referring to the surgeons at the hospital 'carving' me up. I guess that we are the little people and perhaps the horse is Josh's courage. I am so very grateful for this vital help when we were sinking. Josh's comments later confirm how this helped him:

'Jonathan really helped. By the third week, I had stopped having fights 'cos I got to get to do what I really liked and I had never been able to do this before – using clay', and the teachers at school helped me a lot too'.[5]

[5] See Appendix E for more information on Child and Adolescent Mental Health

13

Post Mastectomy Sex – Wow!

10th November 05: I find it a comfort to go to church sometimes on Sundays, but more often I attend Early Morning Prayer before work at 8.30am on weekdays and short midday service whenever I can make it. Sometimes at midday, there are only one or two people, or sometimes six and up to ten at times. This is more intimate. Today, there are a few of us. To my left, there is someone I have not seen before. I can feel his presence throughout the service, which is an odd sensation. I cannot quite shake it off. Remember, I have not even thought of 'a man' in any way since my mastectomy and diagnosis. It is as if my womanhood/sexuality was annihilated first when I was diagnosed and then, less surprisingly, when I had my mastectomy. I do remember something in me 'cutting out' when the Breast Cancer Consultant told me that this was 'Cancer'. So the thought of meeting anyone again has been the furthest thing from my mind and really of little importance in the grand scheme of things. But unknown to me, this is all about to change!!!!!!!!

I cannot believe that my body is having different sensations from those of the past year and a half. Gosh, I am physically attracted to this man! I feel sexually attracted – where are these urges springing from?

And guess what, for once in my life I do not care about the future – what a relief! I do not care if we are going to build a relationship. I am not interested in settling down and making a commitment – what a different attitude! It feels really good and liberating – wow! I want to go to bed with this man! I have forgotten all about my mastectomy and that is terrific in itself! But slowly I realise that I will have to explain my surgery to him beforehand. Then of course I can't do that without explaining my Breast Cancer. What a start! How do I begin to do this and how will he react! This is still a big deal for me but I want to have sex! So, funnily enough, the moment presents itself – over lunch in a cosy pub restaurant. I take a deep breath and spit it out as simply as I can, while holding on to my emotions at the same time... and guess what, he suspects it! How does anyone suspect this! Still he does and that is good enough for me at this stage. However, I want to wait a few days to make sure he is sure.

In my last year at grammar school I do not have a partner to invite to the school formal. This is being held in the Guildhall, in the centre of Derry, and is a big occasion. I so want to go. Everyone seems to have boyfriends. I have not had a boyfriend yet. Mustering up all my courage, I decide to go alone. Wearing a pretty yellow cotton dress with white lace collar, I take a deep breath and walk in through the imposing entrance and present my invitation. I see some of my friends but feel out of place on my own. Still I am determined to have a good time. The music is great and I want to dance but have to wait patiently, very patiently until someone asks me. Before my anxiety has time to take firm hold, a tall dark-haired, handsome American boy with smiling eyes asks me to dance. I am so excited and relieved. As the music pounds out through the enlivened hall, Pat and I dance and dance non-stop. I am now part of this occasion: no longer outside of it. Feeling free as a bird for the first time, my body twists and twirls rhythmically to the infectious beat of the music. Pat and I have the best fun in the world this evening.

18th November 05: And so we decide to go to bed together. My Breast Cancer has not put either of us off – whoopee! And what an incredible unexpected relief! However when I remove my bra in bed in the dark, I freeze. So almost instinctively, I put it back on, as I feel less vulnerable with my prosthesis protecting my scar on my heart side. We are then able to make love comfortably, baring my whole right breast. After all, I do still have one that works, so to speak. And what a super feeling to know that my body still can 'make love' after what it has been through. I have thought that the surgeon had not only removed my breast but also removed my sexuality. What a lot of power to give to one consultant!

I now reclaim this power. In fact I did not know that I felt this way until this unexpected, surprising experience. This is an amazing 'hurdle' to overcome. I had not even considered a relationship again. I feel terrific and a whole woman again, regardless of whether I have one breast or two and whether this encounter has a future. I don't really care. I am thrilled to bits with myself! It is clear to me that my mastectomy has affected me much more psychologically/emotionally than physically. In fact, when our relationship breaks up a few months later I do not feel disappointed, but realise that this has all been about facing and overcoming 'a huge hurdle'.

Pat and I have three months together before he has to go back home to the States. We dance as much as we can and it's wonderful. This afternoon mammy is out and we sneak up to daddy's bed and creep under the sheets, cuddling and kissing. The key turns in the front door downstairs. We both leap out of bed, riddled with guilt, and try to look completely innocent. Our flushed cheeks give us away. Mammy is angry. Pat hastily leaves. I feel dreadful. No word from Pat for several days. I leap to the phone each time it rings, hoping and praying it is Pat. As time goes on without contact, I feel that I have done something really bad and that Pat no longer wants to know me. Self-loathing slowly eats into my bones, leaving me lost and alone. Out of desperation, I get on the bus and make my way to the cemetery. Eventually I find daddy's unmarked grave and falling to my knees I beseech daddy to make everything alright between Pat and I. 'Please daddy, don't let Pat leave me because I cuddled him under the sheets in your bed. I didn't mean to do anything wrong'.

14

Dis-ease

According to Bach, who created Bach Flower Remedies, the term 'dis-ease' implies a dis-ease within the person themselves, yet always only the 'manifested' illness is treated, not the person and the possible root causes of the illness. My search for this complete healing governs many of my actions over the next couple of years, leading me eventually to The Issels Clinic in Mexico. More about Issels and Mexico later in our story. I wonder when, if ever, health professionals will adopt a pro-active approach to healthcare in this country, rather than this 'reactive' approach of treating only the physical disease itself and ignoring the possible causes. In other words, if we cannot see it, we cannot treat it!

25th November 05: As my friend Auriel and I wait to see my oncologist, I am keen to hear if I am HER2 Positive. The test was done about three months ago. After a thorough physical examination, with no surprises, I ask about the test results. I am given the explanation that these test results have not come through yet, and that it is unlikely that I am HER2 positive as I have an oestrogen receptive Cancer. I am annoyed and insist on having the test results nevertheless. Thirteen weeks have now passed. How long can it take to test my tissue, which they already have at the other hospital from my previous operations?

23rd December 05: At last, my test results are through... and I am HER2 positive. I agree to have a CT scan of my lungs, liver – and my head (my suggestion). My oncologist eventually agrees to start me on Herceptin immediately. What she does not know, but possibly senses, is that I will kick up blue murder if I am refused Herceptin at this late stage.

2006

9th February 06: I am off today to the hospital again for my scan results, not really expecting a clear result. I am getting used to this and never really believe that 'all clear' means that the Cancer has gone. I have always felt that my Cancer is with me for the rest of my life: for me, it means living my life in a way that contains it. At least, that's how I feel at this moment in time.

So off I go on my own this time – a huge step after feeling so terrified when I was initially diagnosed back in May 2004. I am almost a different person. I am continually amazed at my inner strength, becoming brighter and stronger day by day. Well, what is the worst my oncologist can tell me: that I am going to die within a few months! Well, I have already stared death in the face when I was a child. My mother threatened to kill me if I ever told a living soul about what I made daddy do to me. I did so again when I was first diagnosed two years ago and I have lived with it ever since. Now any time is more time to live, not to die. I am not dying till I am on my last legs, until then I am LIVING!! I wish that I could have found this inner strength and increasing contentment when I was a terrified, isolated little child all those years ago in Derry. What I have come to realise is that the light within me was only 'hidden' back then, not extinguished. Cancer has helped me uncover that light and allow it to shine more brightly by the minute. Sometimes when faced with little hope, if we just find the courage to look deep within ourselves, we will find a beautiful essence waiting to radiate. Gosh, listen to me – if it were that easy! This is one long, often painful, self-effacing process, which I imagine, will be lifelong, but it brings longer and longer periods of peace and harmony.

The news is very mixed. No sign of Cancer in my bones, liver and head but there are small nodules and a little fluid in my lung, which may be partly due to radiotherapy or the start of secondaries – the next bombshell! Why did I come on my own, this time of all times? I feel very alone with very important decisions to make. How will I know I am making the right one? I want someone's hand to hold until I feel grounded again.

Although this time I feel somewhat differently. In the beginning I felt that every decision I made about my treatment was critical to whether I lived or died; whereas now I am becoming more sure of my self and my Cancer. I have lasted this long, I am sure that I will last a bit longer, regardless of what decision I make. So I quickly decide to have the fluid drained, provided I can be sedated. I also decide to start Herceptin immediately. I do not feel that I can deal with chemotherapy as well as changing my hormone drugs. I am also seeing Simi – my wonderful wholistic doctor who treats me with vitamin and mineral infusions, photon laser treatment and active oxygen, giving me a great sense of well-being. It is becoming important to me to gain a balance between my medical and complementary treatment. I feel that complementary treatment is building me up whilst the medical treatment is geared to killing the Cancer and stopping it spreading without little consideration for my emotional and spiritual state. I realise that there is no foolproof solution.

Now well into our teens, it's Saturday night and Geraldine and I are getting dolled up to go dancing at our local dance hall, 'Borderland', some eight miles away. Mammy keeps urging me to meet 'someone' although I am not really bothered. I just want to have some fun. Entering Borderland, Geraldine and I join the great divide – all the boys on one side of the dance floor and all of us girls on the other, with the great, shiny, dance floor in between.

The live band explodes on to the stage sending shockwaves of activity throughout the packed hall. My feet take on a mind of their own, with my body following suit – an unexpected release from my dark world. Dying to leap on to the polished floorboards in front of me, I fight hard to restrain myself, waiting very patiently for someone, anyone to ask me to dance. Unable to hold on to myself any longer, my right foot strides out boldly. Suddenly, I feel a firm tug on the back of my neck, propelling me backwards: 'Stop, you can't do that Jacinta. You must wait until you are asked!' my friend insists, trying to be helpful. So instead I reluctantly spend the whole evening gyrating on the spot on our side of the hall and never crossing that divide.

Disappointed that I never had a proper dance, I get a taxi home. Mammy is still awake and eagerly waiting to hear my news. I slowly admit my failure to meet anyone. Not knowing what is wrong with me, I retreat downstairs to the kitchen and cook up a huge feed for myself of bacon, eggs and baked beans whilst recalling the lively music with a suppressed longing for freedom.

10th February 06: A good friend of mine recently handed me 'A Visible Wound', a moving story of Julie Friedberger's personal journey through breast cancer. Whilst I do not share this author's feelings about the physical affect of her mastectomy, one point leaps out of her book and demands my urgent attention, namely how much time she took off work after her surgery – five months!

When I look back, I am shocked at how little time I have taken off work in my first year of diagnosis. Having endured four operations in 2004, I have only taken eight weeks off in total throughout that first year. What have I been I thinking of? Why have I been struggling to get back to work so quickly after each challenging surgery? Thinking back now, I simply took off just enough time to recover physically from each surgery and then rushed back to work in between each operation as if my life depended on it. Now I realise that this was my way of coping with my illness: but what about my emotional healing! How can I really heal properly if I do not heal emotionally? This scan result helps me finally let go of work and give myself a hugely well-earned break. It is high time that I really start taking excellent care of myself. Only now do I realise that my life depends on my looking after myself, not on my work!

15

'Now, You Shall Truly Dance'

*My sister rings me at home and tells me straight away that mammy is dead.
That's all. She is dead. I am speechless with shock. Before I can ask Deirdre
anything further. She has gone. My horrific, terrifying, cruel mother can
actually die. Three years have passed and I have not seen her. I had to stop
the abuse somehow. This was my way. And now she is gone – just like that.
I did not know she could actually die. She often used the prospect of her
potential death as a threat – another weapon in her arsenal. I could never see
her frailty and weakness. How I wish that I could have seen just a small
glimmer of her vulnerability. Then I might have been able to get in, get close
to her and feel loved. Just once would have been enough.*

11th February '06: Sometimes before going to bed at night,
Josh and I choose a card from a pack of wonderful Healing
Cards, which I received as a present from a friend from work.
Tonight my son chooses a card, which reads:

'Ask for Guidance in seeing the truth concealed in your
personal challenges' When I read the explanation, contained in
the accompanying handbook, with reference to the Muslim
mystic Abu Hamid al-Ghazzali (1058-1111), I feel that this
explanation accurately reflects how I have felt for a long time:

'Illness is one of the forms of experience by which humans
arrive at a knowledge of God. Illnesses are my servants which I
attach to my chosen friends. If we see illness as a messenger of
the Divine, or even as a message from our own body or mind,
then we can shift our focus from the ailment to the meaning it
contains'.

I have Cancer but this time in my life I do not feel a victim.

17th March '06: Suddenly, after almost two years to the day,
I am coldly informed that my job is being made redundant. Of
course, as I am occupying this job, this means that I have to
leave! I break down crying, unable to maintain my composure

any longer. What more can happen? I am so upset and very angry. I want to sue the pants of this organisation. What am I going to do now?

I arrive alone at the hospital in Derry early in the evening straight from the airport. I immediately go to reception and urgently ask to see my mother. The Receptionist asks me which ward. I tell her she is dead and in the mortuary. The mortuary is closed. How can the mortuary be closed? My mother is in there. I have to see her now. A nurse brings me up to the ward where mum died earlier and the Ward Sister shows me into her office. I drink tea and more and more tea while watching this strange person in uniform trying to talk to me. My mother died on this floor yesterday. I want to see her now. Which room was she in? Where is it? I want to see it. A nurse shows me the room allowing me to peep inside briefly. Another poor soul has taken her bed and life goes on, as they say, or is it death goes on?

She died in intensive care after surgery. She had a huge tumour on her bowel. It was malignant. She came round after surgery briefly and they resuscitated her once. She recovered but later it happened again and she died. Her desperate attempt at life had finally ended. All alone. God help her.

18th March '06: My strong, yet little, inner voice guides me to not waste any more time but to constrain my precious energies for the more important, challenges ahead. I heed my gut instinct this time. It has never let me down. I feel privileged to have worked with such a dedicated team of staff in Buckinghamshire, providing valuable support to vulnerable homeless families, and for the strong links we developed with external agencies. This has been the real joy for me.

The prospect of redundancy and reduced income pushes down further on my broken back. This stress can only be feeding my Cancer. Josh and I are already struggling as a family. How are we going to cope with all this?

The Ward Sister lets me know that I can go to see mum in the mortuary. A nurse comes with me. I want to go alone but the nurse insists. I walk in expecting to find my mother in a steel drawer, like on the TV programme 'Quincy'. Instead, her little frame occupies part of a trolley wrapped in a thin white sheet. There has been a post-mortem. The nurse turns down the sheet revealing a cold white face and tiny body that looks nothing like my mother but this is my mother. The redness has left her face. As my lips touch her ice-cold forehead, I stop breathing. I could never dare do this when she was alive. The nurse indicates her hand, to her side beneath the sheet. I touch her hand with mounting terror, believing she will grab me. I cannot get over the last time I saw her three years ago – vibrant, nasty, manipulative and cruel. Now she is stone dead. I would have liked to see the life ebbing from her body. I am envious of my sister who was called to the hospital first of all. Mammy was already dead then but warm. My sister got to feel her body warm. Can this awful woman – my mother really be dead? I am not so sure.

The following day, I return to the mortuary for the journey with mammy to the church. My sister and brother arrive with their cousin Barney. I stayed with mammy's friend Nuala the night before. All her friends are there in this small official room adjacent to the hospital. My friend Aileen is also there. They are all looking at me sadly. This is all so wrong. They do not know the real truth. I feel so angry. This is farcical. My mother was horrendous and I am confused, but relieved she is dead. Nevertheless I am still terrified of her lifeless tiny body. One of the funeral bearers ask me if I would like to have my private time with mammy now as I had previously requested. I approach her inert body, now encased in a coffin as the curtains gently close around us. We are now alone. I have brought some white lilies which I carefully place in the coffin, and tuck some hand written notes down both sides of her body. I wrote these earlier but don't know what I said. I want these letters – my last words to go with her. Then I do what I have dreamed of doing since I heard she had died. Her bazookas now devoid of bullets, I lean over her ominous although lifeless body with half of my body covering hers hoping no one would see. Then I breathe out a massive sigh of relief. She has not grabbed me. I have to be sure you see.

22nd March '06: With redundancy looming in the immediate future, I am trying to find out all about the state benefits to which I am entitled. I have never had to claim benefit before. As I painstakingly negotiate my way through some entrenched attitudes within this decentralised state system, I stumble and falter as I determinedly explain my changing circumstances and the severity of my condition to one benefit office after another trying relentlessly to understand and access the benefits to which

I am entitled. After some challenging, debilitating weeks, one angelic member of staff from The Inland Revenue steps forward and offers to speak and liaise with all benefits offices concerned on my behalf. At last. my persistence is rewarded and my stress eased.

Mum is laid out in the church for her funeral the following morning. I was glad to see my old school friends Geraldine and Aileen. Aileen carefully hands me my mother's nighties – one she was wearing when she died and another new one she brought with her to hospital. I cling tightly to these parts of my mother. I decide to stay in her flat by myself for the evening. My brother, sister and cousin Barney stay at a Bed & Breakfast across town. I feel so separate from them, as if we are not part of the same family. I need to be close to mum. I want to absorb every minute. I open the door to her small, untidy, poorly furnished one-bedroomed flat – my mother's lonely world. This has never felt my home. When daddy died in 1970, mammy eventually sold our home, without telling any of us, for some obscure reason and moved into this one-bedroomed flat. I have not been here for three years. I make my way straight to her bedroom and tentatively open her wardrobe. Here she is, bold as life –a neat row of designer outfits individually covered in polythene bags protecting her carefully manicured outward persona. Sitting at her lone dressing table, I see her meticulously applying her expensive skin lotions and make-up with long, deliberate, repetitive strokes to her face and neck – a vital part of her daily ritual, refined over the years to mask her tormented self. This is the only mother I know. It's safe to be close to her now.

Sitting with my brother and sister in the car on the way to the cemetery after the service, I cannot not take my eyes off mammy's coffin. If I had known that she could actually die, I would not have been so afraid of her. I do not take my eyes off her in case she gets out and escapes. I must see her go down into the ground forever and stay there. Standing at the graveside watching closely as mammy is lowered into this deep dark hole. I throw in some lilies. Here is my mother, the only mother I knew. I do not want her to be gone so suddenly. Perhaps some tiny part of her loved me. I feel so utterly alone, isolated from the rest of my family. As the crowd slowly dissipates, I see my friend Geraldine waiting for me. Geraldine, Aileen and I are going out this evening to eat. But where am I going to stay? I run after my mum's friend Nuala and ask her if she minds my staying with her this evening. I feel lost, as if I don't belong anywhere.

26th March '06: It takes some doing living with continually 'sentencing' appointments at the hospital, although Dr. Lavery's lovely secretary Nancy eases my journey by taking time to email me copies of my blood and scan results. This time I have a reasonably good blood count but with some higher than normal readings indicating possible bone inflammation. I am told that Zoladex has high levels of calcium, which may be influencing this reading. I have to struggle hard to remember that Cancer is here to help me 'live' not 'go under'. If I let poor results get the better of me I will miss the precious gifts Cancer is bringing into our lives. But it is a real test of attitude and power of the mind. Still one of my stronger qualities has always been resilience. This poem illustrates my growing inner strength:

Blaze
Once again I rise from the flames
set to destroy me
and take flight.
I am
Stronger
Glorious
Powerful
Victorious.

By Kirsti A. Dyer, MD, MS

My brother and sister painstakingly clear my mother's last home of her remaining pieces of furniture and other possessions, Deep in thought, I pack some of her designer clothes and her face make-up along with the nightie she was wearing when she died. As I am about to leave her meagre bedroom, my teary eyes almost miss a completely unexpected yet revealing glimpse of her past: 'Incest in the Family' a well-worn battered book bearing mammy's illegible scribbles. God help her poor mind and tortured soul. As we leave her flat for the very last time, I ask my brother if he wants to take the beautifully framed photograph of mammy hanging in pride of place on the lounge wall. He replies: 'No, there's something fake about that'. Dressed in her black velvet ball-gown and standing regally with hands carefully poised, a contrived moment captured by a professional photographer belies insincerity from beyond the grave. I close the door firmly but tearfully on this sad place. At least this is real.

27th March '06: As I have a hard struggle with regular three-weekly infusions of Herceptin both due to my fear of needles and my veins breaking down, I ask my oncologist about having a line fitted. She agrees. Later that same day whilst on the chemo ward waiting for Herceptin, I ask about the different types of lines. One nurse explains that the porth-cath is the easiest and most successful, as it does not need to be flushed through every week. It could be flushed at the same time as I have my Herceptin. It is also inserted just under my skin on my chest and appears like a 10p coin sitting slightly proud. I inquire if any patient on the ward has one inserted. Fortunately there is a lovely patient who kindly lets me have a look at her line. It looks good, barely noticeable and completely sealed under the skin. I get the distinct impression that this type of line is not common in this hospital. However, my oncologist agrees that I can have this line fitted. I then go through my usual preparations for this procedure i.e. pre-op check, ensuring type of sedation, as it is easier on my body and mind to be knocked out for these procedures. Then a few days before surgery, I have a change of heart. Surprisingly this is not due to fear of the procedure itself but more importantly, concern about my attitude. At this moment, my attitude is beginning to wear down and attitude is vital to my healing. Having a line fitted in my chest even when I am not in hospital may prevent me from letting go of being a patient. I decide not to take that risk at this time.

This evening proves to be worth every painful, wretched moment of this trip. I fall apart in the restaurant as mammy's friends keep coming up and offering their condolences and saying how wonderful mammy was. I find this unbearable. My mother was not wonderful. She was psychotic and narcissistic. Her friends only saw her perfected mask of respectability. Ironically, those closest to her got the worst of her. This is all a nightmare. My friends drop me off at Nuala's home about 2.00am. I creep in trying to be quiet. The next thing I hear is her warm voice: 'Hi, is that you Jacinta? Why don't you come in to my room and we can chat a little.' Surprisingly she is wide awake sitting up in bed. I make us both a warm drink and sit on the edge of her bed. I feel very upset and very very angry.

'Why do all mum's friends think she was wonderful when she was just terrible and so cruel Nuala?' to which Nuala calmly responds: 'Try not to think too badly of your mother.' This just makes me feel worse and more frustrated. Why shouldn't I think badly of her? Am I going out of my mind? Am I the only one who sees my mother for who she really was? For the next hour or two, Nuala and I continue in the same vein, she trying to soothe my pain by painting my mother in a good light and my relentlessly insisting that she was quite the opposite. Finally, the words I have wanted to hear for most of my childhood seep from Nuala's lips in a barely audible whisper: 'Well actually, Jacinta, I feel that I have to tell you that there have been occasions when your mother's behaviour towards my eldest daughter has put a great strain on our friendship.' At long last, the confirmation I have needed to hear to ease my misery and confirm my sanity and the huge injustice of it all. I push Nuala to continue. I need to hear more, lots more. As this precious night slowly unfolds, Nuala's reluctant declaration of the truth about my mother's behaviour lightens my broken heart. I find it difficult to hear someone close to my mother confirm my pain, yet I am so glad. It's real I am not going mad. I do not have to feel sorry for my mother because It's her funeral. On the contrary, in a strange way I feel elated. I feel a very special bond with Nuala. She has opened a very creaky, rusted door for me and I can now walk through. I shall always be grateful.

The following morning I wave a reluctant goodbye to Nuala and head off to the airport, with my mother safely stored in the boot. Now I can bring mammy back home with me to England and then gradually let go of her in my own time, for as long as that takes.

29th March '06: I feel very low today. I now have had two doses of Herceptin, one dose of Zoladex and Arimidex. I am considering dropping my house price to push the sale through. Every decision I make at the moment seems to be huge and potentially life-changing. At the same time, I am preparing myself for the scan results tomorrow, followed by another dose of Herceptin. I find these 'loaded' visits to the oncologist, followed immediately with treatment, very taxing and emotionally draining.

I do not know how I would get through this without my family of close, selfless friends.

As I drive out of Derry, I make a detour. I have something I must do before I leave, as I know I shall not be back for a very long time, if ever again. I drive slowly through the huge cemetery gates and park just inside. A surreal stillness pervades this place freezing it in time. I tentatively make my way past the weather-worn tombstones. Guided instinctively, I approach a strangely peaceful scene – a mound of fresh earth bearing some partially wilted flowers. Mammy is here, lying in her wooden coffin five or six feet underground. Can she really be down here after all this time. Will she stay here? I have to be sure, very very sure. I carefully look around to make sure no one else is watching. Then without a moment's hesitation I start leaping on mum's grave. I jump higher and higher each time with a renewed determination to push her further down into the earth. She must not get out …ever.

1st April '06: I promised Josh that I would do what it takes, no matter what that is. Here I am – Miss career lady and superhuman single mother, finally after years and years of suppression of my true self - now deciding to throw in the towel. I give in and put myself in the hands of fate. I take the 'life' route instead. As I leave The Lodge in Aylesbury for the last time today, I feel as if both my arms have been cut off. Yet, at the same time, I feel relieved at not having to focus on my job whilst coping with Cancer treatment, looking after my son and running our home. I am proud yet anxious that I have been able to let the spinning plates fall at last. It has taken me two years finally to realise that coping is not what I need to be doing, giving in and letting go is, effectively putting myself and my family first. Cancer has helped me let go at last.

The Lodge by Josh

'Giving in and letting go'
My Prayer as I leave the Lodge for the last time

Dear God, I am letting go
Please carry me for a while
I've got you little one
I've got you
Will I be all right?
Better than you know
I am letting go and trusting you
I know, now you will truly heal!
I am with you all the way.

2nd May '06: One of my major fears for as long as I can remember is my dread of needles. Yet, Cancer has brought more needles into my life than I can believe at times. Complementary treatment (later in this book) involves even more needles! I know deep within me that this is happening for a reason. I have always been terrified of needles as far back as I can remember especially as a little child. Needles make me think of my father.

In my late thirties, I set off to Ivy House in Warminster (a sister house to Clouds House, a rehab unit for drug addicts) on a five day residential Family Therapy Programme. I am searching. I want to deal with childhood particularly my mother's abuse. Set in the Wiltshire countryside, Ivy house, an unassuming building, reaches out to me, holding a shocking revelation in store. The programme for about 20 of us, including relatives of drug addicts, adult children of alcoholics or drug addicted parents, blends relevant lectures with small counsellor-led group sessions. This afternoon in our group session, whilst the counsellor is speaking, my heart is pounding, my pulse racing. My body stiffens as I muster up all my courage to confront a red haired lady just like my mother. I open my mouth to utter my first brave words and my world collapses around my bare feet: 'No, No, this cannot be happening. No, not Daddy, he can't have, no he wouldn't, not daddy. I cannot see anything. The room crashes in on me. No. No. No'.

Later walking along the corridor in Ivy House, a counsellor stops to ask if I am ok. I nod, trying hard to smile but 'little' me tries desperately to climb into the wall, wanting so badly to disappear. Tears streaming down my face, she takes me to a room nearby and not letting me escape from this nightmare, she confirms: 'If you feel this has happened to you, then it has happened'. But daddy wouldn't, daddy couldn't, not my daddy.

5th May'06 Each time I have any treatment involving needles, whether it is having a mineral infusion from my wholistic doctor, Zoladex injection in my stomach or intravenous Herceptin at the hospital, I am less frightened. I no longer feel fear before the procedure, just during the procedure. This is such a big step forward. I am very proud of myself and of Josh and I as a family. I become stronger internally each time. Aside from my physical healing, and much more importantly to me, I am healing emotionally and becoming much more spiritual in my

112

attitude to life. I love this amazing change and my son Josh loves it too. I feel much calmer and happier in myself, which in turn makes Josh feel more secure. He is more confident and at ease. Each day, we both grow stronger, both individually and as a family. Now I am beginning to glimpse a future – wow!

Many months after mum's death, probate comes through, and with it another toxic piece of my mother: her jewellery. Expensive diamond rings, brooches, nine and eighteen carat gold chains and bracelets, watches – rarely worn but kept in a deposit box in the local bank. Mum had come to life again. Now what do we do? How are we going to dissect her peacefully? I travel to my sister's home in Northern Ireland. Mum is laid out on her dining table. Together, with my brother on the phone in the States, we slowly agree to divide this remaining but powerful part of our mother. I often recall my mother fiddling with her diamond rings on her fingers on those rare occasions when she would wear them. Then she would immediately cruelly taunt my sister and I with vain threats of only leaving them to us in her will if we did whatever she wanted. The irony being that now we have them, we do not want them. We never did. As I return home with my portion of my mother - her Omega watch and some gold rings. I later have this jewellery remade into an 18-22ct gold bangle which I sometimes wear, uncomfortably. I keep the chains. But I struggle for a long time with mum's three stone diamond eternity ring – shall I get rid of it? Part of me cannot bear to have it near me, yet I do not actively attempt to sell it. Perhaps in time I will be able to make my peace with this part of my mother. Until then it rests in my jewellery box, devoid of power over my life.

In the months following mum's death, letting go of my mother proves deeply painful. Firstly my brother disagrees strongly with me over appropriate wording for her tombstone. I do not care about what is 'appropriate' and refuse to have a traditional headstone saying: "In loving memory of my dear mother" and so on. I cannot go along with this charade as it is not true for me. I do not have loving memories. In the end we agree to disagree. Instead, I find a beautiful extract from 'The Prophet' by Kahlil Gilbran, born in Lebanon, a poet, artist and philosopher; 1883 – 1931:

For what is it to die but to stand naked in the wind and to melt into the sun?
And what is to cease breathing, but to free the breath from its restless tides, that it may rise and expand and seek God unencumbered?
Only when you drink from the river of silence shall you indeed sing.
And when you have reached the mountain top, then you shall begin to climb.
And when the earth shall claim your limbs, then shall you truly dance.

I have my own little five-sided stone especially made bearing the words: 'Now you shall truly dance' which rests proudly in the centre of my mother's grave in front of my brother and sister's, 'In loving memory etc…' Mammy loved dancing, yet sadly never experienced the real dance of living. Now I believe she can.

16

Fired Out Of A Rocket!

A single professional lady now forty-three years old back in 1994 I walk confidently into my nearest doctor's surgery to register and make my proud announcement: 'I am pregnant'. I am quickly ushered in to see a doctor, who asks me if I have had a pregnancy test, to which I assertively reply: 'No, but I know I am pregnant. I can feel it.' Being pregnant at forty-three raises alarm bells for everyone, as I am now categorised as an 'older' mother, and a single mother at that. I feel quite young, really, and thrilled to bits with myself.

My initial excitement at being pregnant is quickly diluted as I make my way to my first hospital appointment with the consultant — a priority for older mothers. Mammy's words reverberate loudly in my ears: 'You will never have a child: or if you do, it will not be normal' I might have a Down's Syndrome baby. What will I do? How will I manage? A feeling of slow-mounting dread consumes me. Feeling fragile and vulnerable, I wait tentatively in the busy waiting room. I fly out of my chair as I hear my name booming out over the loudspeaker system. Feeling less like an adult and more like a terrified little girl, I approach reception to face my sentence. A burly, red-faced man in a stiff, white coat with an official, grave demeanour beckons me into his austere office. Without any warning, he starts firing: 'You have a one in forty-three chance of having a Down's Syndrome baby. A blood test will only increase these odds. I suggest you have an amniocentesis, but be prepared to terminate if it proves positive'. Frozen with shock, bereft of all breath, I stare ahead, aware of nothing. This is not happening to me. I feel a warm hand on my shoulder, I feel the floor beneath my feet; my lungs finally grasp some vital air. Without a word, I leave this 'courtroom' and walk for hours in the sunshine, my mind ablaze with all sorts of wild thoughts. What will I do?

'You will never have a baby, or if you do it will not be normal' glares my mother as she spews out her sick mantra over and over again. She continues to dig her knife in even further by explaining the painful hours and

hours of labour she endured to have me. Her poisonous tirades seep into my young impressionable mind. I am terrified of childbirth and vow never to have children. What is wrong with me? Why do I cause mammy so much pain? Does she know something I don't? So many questions with no answers. What have I done wrong?

Frantically picking up pace, everything swirling and swirling around in my overcrowded head. I am now almost home, having walked for ages, feeling tired and beginning to slow down. For no reason, I stop, with the busy world swirling around me. A divine feeling rises from the very pit of my stomach and feeds my being. 'I shall be just fine. I will not kill my baby because I don't like it, I am blessed to be pregnant at all and I am going to celebrate every minute of this miraculous time in my life.' My little girl is at rest and I have taken over with a strength and faith that I did not know I had until this point.

As my body expands and I put on the pounds, I feel wonderful. So very proud of myself. I feel beautiful. I only return to the hospital for standard checks, for example blood pressure. After forty-three years on this planet, I am now part of the baby world and feel I fit in and belong. I have already decided that my baby is a boy and have already named him Joshua.

Now in my thirty-fourth week of pregnancy, I am packing to drive up north to Preston, Lancashire to conduct a two day training course in management development skills. Afterwards I will stop in Mansfield, Nottinghamshire on the way back, to run a one-day customer care programme. This is my last training before Josh arrives. But all this is about to change.

On my way out the door, I telephone Anne, my midwife, to let her know that, as I have missed my last check-up, perhaps I should come in to see her soon. On hearing my immediate plans, she offers to call round to see me there and then. Cases by the door, everything checked, I am ready to leave. Fifteen minutes later, the doorbell rings. Hovering with anticipation, I explain to Anne my urgency to get on my way. She calmly comes in and, asking me to sit down, quickly takes my blood pressure. As I get up to leave, thanking her for coming, her firm hand on my arm stops me in my tracks. 'Your blood pressure is high, Jacinta, and you need to rest'. I reply with mounting anxiety: 'I will be able to rest when I finish my work'. 'You need to go into hospital for a few days until your blood pressure comes under control'. I can't move or think or anything. Life as I know it has come to an abrupt halt.

After my last surging blood pressure reading, my midwife is coming to see me every day at home to check my vital signs. My friend Ginny is staying with me for the weekend and we are having a lovely time, taking photos of my huge belly. Anne arrives looking official with blood pressure monitor to hand. I reassure her that my blood pressure is probably fine, as I feel relaxed and happy. Smiling disingenuously, paying lip service to my cheeriness, she promptly seeks my arm and wrapping the band tightly around it, she starts pumping. Focused intently on the monitor gauge, her eyes darken and looking up at me trying to smile, she issues her alarming news yet again: 'I am afraid Jacinta that your blood pressure is up again. You will need to go back to hospital now, can your friend go with you? I will follow in my car. I shall call an ambulance right away' All I can hear are 'hospital' 'now' and 'ambulance'. The paramedic tries to keep me calm, which proves to be quite a challenge, given my racing hormones and raging blood pressure. My whole world is turning upside down and I can do little about it. I am anxious now. Sitting in the back of the ambulance, the paramedic's constant attempts to engage me in conversation start to irritate me. Upon arrival at hospital, I am immediately confined to bed and sedated. I realise now that my body is struggling and that my baby will soon be here. Quietly in bed, gently massaging my growing bump, I have a little reassuring word with Josh: 'Darling pet, all will be okay and you will soon be here in my arms. Just relax, pet, and stay inside mammy for a little while longer if you can. I love you darling'. The following morning I feel low. Watching all the parents and partners coming to see their daughters and wives and girlfriends leaves me feeling very alone and upset. Knowing I have good friends around me eases this pain and helps me see the reality. If my parents were alive, mammy would only have terrible things to say to me and daddy would go along with mammy and say very little. After the consultant comes to see me and prods my growing mound, he mentions that I am having a small baby and may need to be induced soon if my blood pressure continues to rise. I just want to go back home and get ready. This is happening too fast.

Later the same day, I feel strongly that I am not going to make it. As I make my laboured way to the bathroom, I see mammy on the ward wearing the nightie she wore when she died seventeen months earlier. She is happy to see me and welcomes me with open arms. My logical mind knows she is dead but my present state of anxiety is telling me otherwise. She wants me. Caught between two worlds, I ring my sister in Ireland, urgently telling her in one breath that I am not going to make it, explaining clearly that there will be complications, the surgeon can only save one of us. Anxiously I make my sister promise faithfully that she will tell the surgeon, when asked, to save Josh. I am sure I will die. I know Josh will be fine. He is strong. As I lie in bed my stomach contorting, I hear another patient in the bed opposite shout for a nurse: 'Can someone come quickly, this lady is in labour'. Gosh, this must be it. I exhale a sigh of relief, thinking this is much easier than I thought it would be. Two and a half hours later, as I am pushing for England, and maybe Ireland, too, squeezing the life out of Claire's poor hand, I hear myself gasping: 'I am not going to make it, I am not going to make it' and then my mantra changes euphorically: 'I'm going to make it, I'm going to make it!'. As my beautiful baby boy emerges from my aching body, I emerge from my mother's skin, elated and amazed to be alive.

Leaving to go home after a week in hospital, I feel proud, yet vulnerable. Even though Josh only weighs 4lbs 13ozs, I feel smaller. Arriving home, the full impact of the past seven days hits me. I left to go to hospital as a single professional lady, now I am returning a single mother, all within one week. I feel as if I have been fired out of a rocket: I have landed in the same place but everything has changed, nothing is in the same place anymore.

17

Letting Go

Why do I struggle so much? I do wonder why I try so hard to keep our home. I will never own it, as my mortgage extends forever! Yet at the same time, I feel an overdeveloped sense of responsibility and obligation to hang on at any price. The cost to me is already apparent. It is time to let go before I leave this house 'in a box!'

Deciding to sell our home relieves me of a great pressure and huge weight – a weight that in some ways I have been carrying since childhood. Yet everyone around us seems to live life in a mortgaged house with a career. I have put our home on the market with several estate agents, but I am still uncertain as to whether I am being too rash! Well, rash is far from it. I deliberate long and hard over this sale, weighing up the pros and cons, listening to the conflict between my head and my heart.

My 'head' says:

'Stay here as you can just about manage. At least you will always have a home which you can then leave for Josh when you die!'

While my 'heart' says:

'What is taking you so long, will you get on with it and have a life? What does it take for you to really let go, to think enough of yourself and Josh to live the life you both deserve? Offload those onerous burdens laid down on your small shoulders since the beginning of time!'

I talk this over again and again with my close friends. Anyone else would have thought I was completely mad! I recall saying to them:

'You see, even if we stay in our home and change it inside, there will still be a major problem! It will always be facing the wrong way! So we have to leave!'

Only a few of my more spiritual friends can really see where I am coming from. I am so lucky to have these spiritual buddies in my life. Deep down, this decision is right for my mental and physical health and ultimately for out quality of life as a family. Making these major lifestyle changes is more challenging in many ways than handling Cancer. Yet ironically Cancer makes all this possible. This is incredibly rewarding and immensely liberating.

The phone rings and rings. Only when I have put Josh down to sleep do I eventually pick up my messages. I quickly ring back my friend, Nuala in Derry, only to miss her yet again. Several days later, Nuala and I finally speak to each other. She has been to mammy's grave and seen my stone in pride of place, glistening in the sunshine. Listening to her caring words, I feel connected to home without any fear of lurking demons. Nuala sounds so thrilled to hear about Josh. The strangest thing being that she was over here seeing her older daughter around the same time as I gave birth. She has helped me more than I could ever have imagined.

A few days later, my school friend, Aileen calls me. I can sense an ominous tone to her voice and immediately ask her what is wrong. Trying to gently prepare me for bad news, Aileen explains that my friend Nuala was found dead at her home early yesterday morning. She had tripped and fallen downstairs during the night. Tears silently trickle down my face. My card thanking her for all her help was found on her bedside table.

17th May 06: I sold our home today (well, I accepted an offer, subject to contract of course). I want to fly and trust the elements completely with Josh. Now watch us go and have carefree fun for a change. Cancer is helping me to let go and trust again. In a way I am grateful to my own mother, who was never able to be close to me in her troubled lifetime. However, in a strange way, she has played a special part here. Through Cancer, she has allowed me to forgive her completely and let us both get on with our lives, here on earth and beyond. George Eliot's saying comes to mind and fills my heart with excitement: 'It is never too late to be what we might have been'

Josh, just 6 weeks old, and I board a flight. I want to bring my baby boy home to Ireland. As I walk down the Strand Road in Derry for the first time since my mother died, carrying my beautiful son in my arms, I feel an overwhelming mix of sadness, regret, pride, triumph and incredible joy, all at the same time – sad and regretful that my mother could not lovingly be by my side, proud of my baby boy and triumphant that I have been able to have my son despite all my mother's frequent forebodings. But above all, regret that this is the only way that it could have been: 'I know mammy that it had to be one or other of us here today. Sadly, you could never allow me to make my own choices and be happy, However sad and alone I feel, I am so proud of Josh any myself today. I do wish you could have been here, too'.

Later today we visit mammy's and daddy's grave. In front of the traditional headstone, my small stone rests proudly in the centre of the overgrown, neglected, grassy plot: 'Now you shall truly dance': A growing pride in my triumphant single motherhood, temporarily erasing deep-rooted sadness, holds us both in its strong, empowering embrace.

Moving quickly past many, more recent graves, I find one where my friend Nuala rests in her lovingly tended plot. I gently place my single white rose below her fresh headstone, quietly whispering: 'Thank you Nuala so much for being there for me when mammy died, for your strength, compassion, precious acknowledgement of my mother's difficult behaviour and for your encouragement and delight at hearing of the birth of my son, I will always remember you'. Even in death, I feel her loving presence holding Josh and I close.

22nd May 06: Today is the first day that I surrender my control to God, asking him to guide me through the day so that I heal. If anyone overhears me talking to myself I am sure they will think that I have 'lost it'. The reverse is the case – instead of 'losing it' as it were, I am 'finding it'. 'It' used to mean status, ambition, career success and material possessions borne out of a relentless inner need to be perceived as successful. Of course, this success could never remove my hidden feelings of loneliness, isolation, dissatisfaction and unhappiness. 'It' now means amazing inner strength, personal power and self-respect which I am discovering day-by-day through confronting my fears and letting go of the need to control. I am beginning to experience a level of self-contentment and peace that I have never known. Most importantly, my healing is helping Josh and I as a family to thrive through Cancer.

Two months after giving birth to my little baby boy, I prepare to return to work. I have a sales training course booked in Oban in Scotland. I cannot really get my head around going away for three whole days working and leaving Josh. The world of training and consultancy seems a million miles away from where I am now. I feel maternal, loving, warm and fulfilled. It seems a very long way to go back, to facilitating lively training workshops, miles and miles from home. However, reluctantly, I start planning my trip, feeling as if I am having to stifle my newfound motherhood in order to revert to this dynamic, independent, working life where I am fully in control. Fortunately, a friend steps in unexpectedly and offers to accompany Josh and I on this first trip. I am relieved. However, the whole experience of being a new mother with my baby boy one minute and then this groomed, professional trainer the next, sits uneasily with me – a unholy alliance. My friend is a great source of support. But instead of focusing my full attention on delivering my training programme, I cannot wait to introduce little Josh to all these strangers at every opportunity. How I wish I could stop working now but, sadly, nagging worries about pressing mortgage payments, ongoing bills, feed my insecurity and need to succeed, driving me on.

The Hand of God by Josh

Josh sketched this picture on the Euro star coming back from a weekend away in Brussels. Jesus' wings look so comforting, holding him as he suffers on the cross for us.

15th June 06: As time passes, I am becoming more and more empowered. I value and trust my wholistic doctor's advice and treatment. I find myself replying to my friend's disapproving comment on my tucking into a big bar of chocolate: 'At the end of the day, my life is my own and I choose what I do with it'. Now I am finding my feet and feeling in control, in a totally different way to before'.

20th June 06: Looking back over the past two years, having got over the unbelievable initial shock, 'physical' Cancer itself is okay but dealing with my own feelings as they arise day-to-day is the real challenge and revelation. This helps me to talk to Josh as honestly as possible about what is happening to us both in many ways. As we move through Cancer, the passage is becoming easier, smoother and incredibly revealing, opening up so many new doors. My world does not 'rock' or tumble down anymore when I see my oncologist and hear her next indictment. As I said to her recently: 'It matters less and less what you say to me. I do not let your words have power over my life any longer.'

26th June 06: Last night, I had a frightening dream: I was in a field initially with two male friends. One asked what we thought of the field. I was trying to look beyond the surface for the deeper meaning. All of a sudden, the scene was enclosed within a room. The ground dropped away leaving me rooted to an 18-inch wide grass verge with sheer drops on either side. I could not move, as I would certainly die or be terribly injured if I fell off either side. I yelled to my friends to call the fire brigade. Neither of my two friends bothered much. Perhaps they could not see what was happening! Then I took a step forward, deciding to risk it. I managed to reach the kitchen sink (at the end of the verge) and climb up to safety. Such is the extent of my deep-seated fear of moving forward in my life. But I know deep inside that I can move on with Josh, leaving all fears, struggles and feelings of loneliness behind me. We are due to exchange at the end of July.

10th July 06: Today my friend Rachael, her son Joey, Josh and I go for a long walk up to Waddesdon Manor – a lovely National Trust property in beautiful grounds just ten minutes from our new home. The boys want to go and play together, so we go our separate ways, agreeing to meet up later at 3.00pm. However, Rachael and I start chatting and forget the time. Josh rings me on his mobile and then I realise that it is 3.30pm, half an hour later than we agreed. I feel terrible. I reassure Josh and Joey that we will come and meet them as quickly as possible and not to worry, just stay where we agreed. We both leave our coffee and make our way to our meeting place. Of course now we are even later. Josh is unsettled and anxious, more so than I thought he would be. In a later meeting with Jan - the family therapist, we discuss this incident, as it has been preying on my mind. I have not connected Josh's anxiety on this occasion in any way to our unsettling life changes. Just as I wobble from time to time with everything going on, Josh also wobbles. It just manifests itself differently. It's hard to realise this at times as I am trying to keep my head above water. Josh, myself and Cancer are all in this together. We have to keep communicating with each other to get through this bumpy time and emerge stronger for it.

Mum Going Away **by Josh**

Josh made the following comment regarding my Cancer when he sketched this picture: 'It has given me a lot more time with mum because she used to travel a lot'.

12th July 06: I attend morning prayers with Anne from church. We take it in turns to read various readings from the bible. The following passage strikes chords for me:

'Nevertheless, there will be no more gloom for those who were in distress. In the past he humbled the land of Zebulun and the land of Naphtali, but in the future he will honour Galilee of the gentiles, by the way of the sea, along the Jordan: The people walking in darkness have seen a great light; on those living in the land of the shadow of death, a light has dawned. You have enlarged the nation and increased their joy; they rejoice before you as people rejoice at the harvest as men rejoice when dividing the plunder. For as in the day of midians defeat, you have shattered the yoke that burdens them, the bar across their shoulders, the rod of their oppressor. Every warrior's boot used in battle and every garment rolled in blood will be destined for burning, will be fuel for the fire. For to us a child is born, to us a son is given and the government will be on his shoulders. And he will be called wonderful counsellor, mighty God, Everlasting father, prince of peace.'

Isaiah Chapter 9 verses 2-6

Josh experiences what we are going through at a deep level and whilst he is not always able to put his feelings into words, he expresses himself wonderfully through his art and his special gifts to me. Later today, Josh buys me a special birthday present – a beautiful carved wooden angel of miracles.

14th July 06: Having seen my oncologist today for the results of a third scan of my lungs and liver, I am unnerved on arriving at the hospital with Auriel. I am seen immediately. I have been used to long waits of an hour or more. I immediately assume this means bad news and I will be rushed into hospital again. All those uncertain, traumatic weeks of 2004 come flooding back to me. I burst out crying before I have even seen my oncologist. Then she calmly walks in smiling and uttering that everything is fine. I cannot take this in; in fact it takes me a good twenty four hours to digest this information. Of course, it does not mean that

I am well, but it does mean that the treatment is working and everything is moving in the right direction. The one nodule on my lung is steadily decreasing. And with all the life changes I am making, I know that this can only get better. In fact, when I go to the ladies before leaving, I gently thank God. For a very fleeting moment, I can see for the first time, that there is a distinct possibility that I may be able to put 'Cancer' behind me – a wild thought that I have not even considered before.

20th July 06: My disability-parking badge arrives today in the post. How strange. One minute a career woman and super mum, now 'disabled'. I feel a cheat using my disability badge, yet I know that I am not. I do value the help that easier accessible parking is giving me. On those days when my energies are very low, being able to park near the shops that I need is wonderful and eases the added stress of finding parking. Believe me, all the effort and challenge involved in completing the Disability Living Allowance form – the most difficult part of this process, has been worth it. Once I manage to rise above the stigma of 'disability', I feel relieved and more positive. In fact, my disability-parking badge feels more like a 'perk' than a stigma.

3rd August 06: Early this morning Josh comes into my bedroom and notices 'Squidgy' on my bed. He picks it up and starts playing with it, which is quite comical to watch. Then he remarks: 'Mum, Squidgy has bubbles in it. I don't think that it's supposed to have those'. I don't pay much attention to my prosthesis, so these bubbles have escaped my attention. I look closely and realise that it is beginning to wear out. Squidgy is sick! I forget just how sensitive Josh can be, particularly concerning my illness. Of course life is changing day-by-day for both of us. This whole experience has dramatically alerted our senses in so many ways. We are much more aware of each other, for obvious reasons. As life stabilises again, I am sure that we will settle into our new life.

Our Home for Sale by Josh

Wrapped up in the sale of our home is 'letting go' of the
past, as far back as childhood. For Josh, it is letting go of the
painful, difficult past two and a half years. We decide to have a
'letting go' celebration and invite a few close friends. I discuss it
with my neighbour Silvia who very kindly suggests we use her
garden, as it fronts on to the lake outside her home. I want to
significantly and symbolically mark our farewell to the past. Josh
and I make a list of all the things we will leave behind as we
move on. My own list includes: Fear, Money worries, Stress,
Loneliness, Single life, Career, Ego I almost forget to add my
Cancer. When I consider my list further, I realise that I have

already added my real Cancer. Josh keeps his own list private, so I do not pry. This is difficult for Josh, as this has been the only home he has ever known and for him, too, it is a step into the unknown – so much for my darling boy to deal with at such a tender age. We then write down each word on a separate piece of paper, which we carefully fold and place in a wooden box, which Josh had made with his godfather, Martin. Josh and his friend, Joey, tape five Lego men to the top of the box. As time approaches, I feel quite nervous but determined to do this. Our friends arrive and we move down to the water's edge. Martin pours some petrol on the box, ignites it and sets it on the water. As we all stand round, Josh and I together hand-in-hand, gentle tears trickling down my face, I watch my painful past slowly sink below the surface of the cool, dark lake water. The pain of the past fades. Afterwards, we celebrate together. Josh plays happily with his friend Joey.

Later this evening, I watch a film, which moves me greatly, 'The Shawshank Redemption'. This film tells the tale of how a highly intelligent married banker, wrongfully imprisoned for 19+ years for killing his wife and her lover, wins the hearts of his fellow prisoners and the trust of the prison staff. His work within the prison involves building a library and providing education courses for the prisoners, as well as doing all the accounting and banking for the prison staff. His story illustrates how hope gives him life, ultimately resulting in his escape to a new, cleaner life.

14th August 06: This evening my friend Anne spends some time with Josh while I have a belated evening farewell dinner with my wonderful staff from work. When I come home, Anne has drawn a picture of a 'J' shackled with chains. I notice that the chains appear loose. 'J' could be both Josh and myself. With Anne's continuous encouragement, support, and her practical help in enabling Josh and I physically to move home, I have been able to shed some of these chains. I never thought it could be possible to let go. Without Cancer, I do not think I would have reached this conclusion, and if I had, it would have taken so much longer. I feel exhilarated to be leaving now that I have got over my agonising decision-making. Of course, for Josh it is a very different situation. Even though he does not have any friends here to play with after school, I am sure that he will miss his first home. As he says himself: 'It has kinda affected the money and now we have to sell our house 'cos of all the tablets and I don't really like leaving even though I don't have any friends here and they are all on Fairford Leys'. He surprises me when he adds that he will miss everyone here and goes on to describe our neighbours. His power of observation takes some beating:

'Well, mum, there is strange Jim and Anne opposite, cranky Margaret and John next door, kind, friendly Silvia, the odd lady at the end who never comes out, plastic face Linda, two houses I do not know and healing Simi' I express surprise that he will miss them. He wisely responds: 'But they are who are around us!'

The night before we move, we have very little furniture left at home. We bring an old mattress down to the lounge and Josh settles there with his sketchpad and pencils. In less than an hour, my 11-year-old son sketches the following three moving pictures showing the true impact of everything on him.

Nightmares by Josh

Don't Be Afraid of Death by Josh

Everything Hurts **By Josh**

However, leaving our own home fills me with dread. It's as if here I am, as an adult and not a child anymore, standing in the open doorway of my childhood home with everything ahead of me: yet I am unable to move, so frightened that I will fall and die if I go through this doorway. Yet I know I must, I want to and I will.

17th August 06

Letting Go **by my friend and artist Rachael Westlake**

This sketch captures little me taking a frightening leap of faith. Cancer has shown me the way out of my own prison and stunted existence. The gentle hand breaking my fall turns out to be more wondrous than I could ever have imagined.

We are Moving!

The Phoenix
by Rebecca Wiles

Beautiful, glorious and sacrificing self for renewal
You build a pyre and set yourself ablaze!
For the sake of self, red bird of fire,
You come forth through your ashes a new bird shedding the
old self
Which no longer is needful, you embrace your new strength
and fly to the heights of the sky to the city of the sun
and give the ashes unto the altar of the sun god for your
immortality
Embrace yourself for you are a child of the sun
and will live eternal through birth, death and renewal.
The spirit never dies!

'Letting go of the old and embracing the new
with excitement, trust, commitment and deep gratitude'

18

Immersion

12th September 06: I have quite a revelation when I go along to see my new local Doctor for the first time, to have my Zoladex injection. I go alone feeling quite confident. I briefly explain the past few years, indicating that I now feel that I am over the worst 'emotionally' re Cancer – at least that's what I feel right now! In fact, nothing will ever feel so terrible as it did at the beginning of the 2004 when I was initially diagnosed. My new doctor mentions my fear of needles but, for the first time, I find myself explaining that it is not 'needles' that are the problem but the situation i.e. here I am with a doctor whom I do not know, who is a 'man' no less, (which he confirms rather proudly) and he is about to 'inject' me.

Daddy and I are in mammy's and daddy's bedroom and I have daddy all to myself. Today is a bit different. Daddy and I are doing different things. I don't understand. I don't really like doing this but as it's daddy it must be alright.

Suddenly the bedroom door bursts open. Mammy comes in, carrying my baby sister and holding my little 3-year-old brother's hand, her back arched, her bazookas pointed. I feel hurt and cold as daddy immediately backs away, leaving me standing naked in the middle of the room, trying hard to cover myself. Mammy's face contorts as she glares at daddy, who is skulking in the far corner. Then her virulent gaze infects my naked body. I know something terrible has happened but I don't know what. Alone and desperate, my bare body starts uncontrollably shaking. Why has daddy left me? Why will he not come to get me and give me my clothes? Why is he hiding? An unnatural paralysis creeps over my ruined body, rooting me to the spot, against my desperation to run away and hide.

'What have you done, Cinty? Why did you make daddy do that?' I still don't know what I have done wrong. 'This is all your fault'. I feel my insides slowing being crushed and breaking into small pieces. An unbearable shame

seeps through every bone in my little body, hurting me all over again. 'Take
her downstairs out of my sight' Daddy obeys without looking at me. An
ominous silence separates us as we go down to that awful place again.
Shaking all over, clutching my damaged clothes, I say to myself over and over:
Will Daddy stop loving me? Will he not cuddle me anymore?

I have not realised how much I have healed until this
experience. I explain to my doctor how best to approach this
procedure. This must sound very odd to this doctor, although he
simply listens and seems to understand: 'Well, you see, doctor,
what works best is this: I have put some Emla cream on my
stomach in advance to numb that area. If you can then give me a
local injection to further numb the area and after that the
Zoladex itself. But you need to tell me that you are about to do
it. I will then make humming noises while you are doing it, which
you need to ignore. This helps distract me. Then please tell me
when the needle is out!' We then go ahead and amazingly I am
fine. For the first time, I feel complete. No words can explain
how amazing this feeling really is.

22nd September 06: As Simi will be leaving in November, we have agreed that she will give me as many vitamin infusions and active oxygen sessions as possible before she goes. So not only am I having Herceptin through infusion/needle every three weeks, I am now also having two infusions a week with Simi plus my Zoladex injection in my stomach every four weeks as well in all, about ten needles a month. On this visit to Simi, I feel stronger. Needles do not seem to have the same power over me. They can hurt, but dealing with physical pain has always been easier for me.

3rd December 06: When Canon Tim Higgins left St. Mary's Church in Aylesbury to move to Bristol Cathedral one year ago, I felt very upset. He has been a real tower of strength for me at an awful time. I know he has had to move on in his work but there is 'little me' who wished he would stay and not abandon me. It has taken me twelve months to put pen to paper. By writing to Tim, I have been able to separate and let go.

Why will daddy never give cuddle me anymore. I keep waiting for him to come up from his office downstairs but he just looks at me and smiles sadly like he does not mean it. What have I done wrong? I love him but he does not want me anymore. I keep trying to help him with mammy when she is in her bad moods but, no matter what I do, he never looks happy to see me. I feel so awful inside, but I am scared to let anyone see.

Dear Tim

I have thought about you often since you left St. Mary's and I have to say that it has taken me all this time to put pen to paper. You were a tower of strength and source of inspiration to me at the time. Your departure left a gaping hole in my life, as I know you knew and understood. I have a confession to make – I didn't go back to St. Mary's for a service of any kind until June, when I went with Anne for morning prayers at 8.30am. It was strange without you there. I often look at the cross you left as your gift before you left. It hangs above the little font by the candle stand. Do you remember my talking to you about possibly selling my home on Watermead, due to overpowering financial pressures? Well I did in the end. It just felt so right. We moved to Waddesdon in August this year. Our new home is wonderful and, strangely enough, I feel so much more secure here even though we have so much less. Josh has started secondary school here in Waddesdon and is settling in quite well, although it is quite a leap from his last school. He is a different boy these days, much more secure and confident. Our lives have stabilised at long last!

As far as my health goes, well this is an ongoing business, but no longer frightening, nor is it in control of me anymore. I currently have the intravenous drug Herceptin every three weeks at the hospital, which is proving effective. Scans are showing a reduction in a cyst on my lung and my blood tests are good and stable although my oncologist has mentioned that WHEN this stops being effective, she has alternative suggestions for me, which sounds ominous. I am sure chemo is lurking somewhere. Whether I will go there is another matter. It seems that the Cancer is still with me but not 'active' any longer. I do not like or accept the 'assumed' progression of this disease. I am not diseased anymore: I live life more 'easily' each day and enjoy it. Josh and I are closer and stronger. I do not intend for Cancer to stay with us. I have changed and my Cancer is now doing the same. I would not have had this attitude two years ago. I also find myself becoming quieter in myself.

I feel very grateful to have reached this point of stillness to live life easily and being able to be here for Josh – not so busy rushing about, doing so much, yet achieving very little. I am no longer frightened of anything and Cancer no longer has a grip of our lives. Josh recently described where we are 'at' – perfectly, I thought: he started sketching a picture for our book, 'Hidden Gifts', and explained to me that he wanted to do a scene showing the end of the war, with some soldiers killing off the last of the bad guys and others holding their rifles high above their heads triumphant! Isn't that just beautiful? He has not finished it, so perhaps there is more work and healing to do. We could not have achieved all this without your help and unfaltering support. Thank you.

19th December 06: While the Issels Clinic is in the back of my mind as complementary treatment, I want to make sure that I have looked at possible solutions closer to home. I feel drawn to Issels. I decide to call my friend Dr. Rosy Daniel, who has been a great support to me. Dr. Daniel, of Health Creation – a wonderful, knowledgeable, doctor with a refreshing wholistic approach to Cancer. I have seen Rosy at her clinic in Bristol early in 2005 and spoken to her several times on the telephone. Talking through my current concerns with her, she explains how complementary cancer treatment approaches fall broadly into seven levels:

LEVEL 1 – Nutritional Metabolic
LEVEL 2 – Herbal
LEVEL 3 – Immunotherapy in Europe
LEVEL 4 – Intravenous Metabolic
LEVEL 5 – Physical Therapies
LEVEL 6 – Mind-body Therapies
LEVEL 7 – Health Creation/Health Coaching [6]

Dr. Daniel suggests various alternative sources of wholistic treatment here in the U.K, as opposed to 'fully immersing myself' in The Issels Programme. The phrase: 'fully immersing myself in' leaps out at me. That's exactly what I want – to fully immerse myself in getting well, rather than trying to manage everything else as well! Somewhere, I can totally hand myself over to my healing, where I can completely let go of my day-to-day life, fall apart and consequently heal completely. Anything less may be less costly, but will not be cost-effective for me. I would still be the patient, yet still having to liaise between each different practitioner. I am so tired of having to explain myself, run our

---

[6] See Appendix C1 for further explanation of these levels of Complementary Cancer treatment.

home and cope with Cancer all at the same time. In my darker moments, I express my overwhelming feelings:

Having To
so tired of having to
always having to
not wanting to
have to anymore
free to choose
free to decide
free to refuse
if I want to ride
or take a bus
or stand still
or make a fuss
free to be brave
free to cry
free to decide
if I want to try
to cheer myself up
or fold up and die
for today if I choose
is mine

2007

15th January 07: Before finally deciding to go to the Issels Clinic in Mexico, I want to check out treatment at The Dove Centre, a wholistic clinic in Hampshire, to make sure that I am not being too hasty. My friend Anne accompanies me on the two-hour drive to the clinic. I see Dr. Julian Kenyon who is to the point, very professional, obviously very knowledgeable in his field. He is aware that I am considering going to the Issels Clinic in Mexico. He explains that he can offer me most of the same treatments as Issels and cannot understand why I would put myself under the additional strain of travelling. He looks at my blood under a microscope, showing me how the white blood cells are hardly moving, which is no surprise, given my condition. He also spots a lot of 'gunge' in my blood and then mentions diet. With a pair of headphones on and facing a computer screen called the oberon machine, I then get an indication of potential Cancer in my body – very scary stuff, but at least I know! He agrees that chemo would probably not be very effective in my situation, reducing my bone marrow and weakening me further. Then we are shown downstairs to the friendly nurse who explains the nature of photodynamic therapy, which Dr. Kenyon has recommended. This involves my coming down to Hampshire three days a week over a two week period to go on this machine for one and a half hours at a time. Then I realise that I probably will be too tired to drive to and from home each time. The nurse suggests that I stay locally in a bed and breakfast but alarmingly adds: 'You will need to have someone with you, as there is a risk that you will go into anaphylactic shock with this treatment! This is very frightening. I break down crying – this is when the penny finally drops. I know deep down that I do not need treatments in isolation, no matter how effective they may be, although I might return to the Dove for top-up treatments in the future.[7] I want to be looked after in a supportive, loving environment where I am free to use all my resources, to help myself heal completely. In the car on the way home, I look at Anne and she looks at me: 'Well, Jacinta, it's make-your-mind-up time!' She wisely adds: 'We both know what you are going to do'. Having researched many complementary treatment centres, both in U.K and Europe, I cannot find any centre, apart from Issels in Mexico, which can provide the 'complete range of complementary immunotherapy treatments all under one roof'.

I subscribe to a regular email bulletin from 'What doctors don't tell you'. The following excerpt mirrors and reinforces my feelings and my decision to go to Mexico:

---

[7] See Appendix F at the end of this book for further information on The Dove Clinic

'A sizable body of research concerns terminal Cancer patients (which I am not) who, with little or no medical intervention, end up beating the odds. What these cases collectively say about Cancer is highly instructive. In case after case, they describe people up against a major roadblock in their lives: an unremitting stress; an unresolved trauma; a prolonged hostility; a marked isolation; a profound dissatisfaction; a quiet despair.

They describe people who are boxed into a corner with no apparent way out, people who have lost their role as the central protagonist in their own life drama. They are people, who, in short, hurt deeply in their very souls.

Those people who beat their Cancer, whose survival remains unexplained, are those same individuals who find a way out of the corner. They get rid of the source of the psychological heartache, whether that means resolving a problem with their mother, divorcing an abusive spouse, leaving a dead-end job. They take full responsibility for their illness.

But most important of all, they find the lost meaning in their lives. They find a path back to their joie de vivre. For these patients, the question is getting to the heart of the Cancer in their souls.'

Before undertaking such a comprehensive treatment as the Issels Programme, I speak to a patient from U.K who had just returned from Issels. Our conversation further influences my decision. I also have many questions to ask Issels directly, which they happily answer in detail. I email my questions to Terry Burke, their representative, and she rings me to discuss my concerns as often as I need.

After much reading, probing and consideration and a strong gut feeling, I decide to go to the Issels Clinic for twenty-eight days, where I shall receive the best in wholistic, non-toxic immunotherapy treatment, designed to build my immune system to overcome my Cancer. This centre will treat me physically, and support me lovingly and spiritually, allowing me to let go completely and heal intrinsically. Almost three years since diagnosis, I have found what I believe that I truly need to heal! I remember saying to my son outside the school gates two and a half years ago, as we both sat crying together in my car: 'Darling, I will do all that I feel it takes to get myself well. I will get well!'

I could never have imagined that might mean my going away to Mexico, of all places, without my son. This has been a very difficult decision to make. At my low moments, I feel that I am leaving 'my very life blood' to 'gain my life blood'. No matter how difficult, I know this is the right decision for us. I just wish that I could have some 'little' decisions to make to balance the scales for a moment, but I guess these will come later.

19

Expurgating the Beast

'The Beast' I realise is MY BEAST – a hellish mixture of a punishing past, poor self esteem, lack of love for myself and for others, lack of inner peace, enmeshed with cancerous cells. I know that I can deal with this and purge my mind, body and soul of my demons once and for all.

I cannot believe that I allowed money to have so much power over me. It had become my god. It is no real surprise that it is part of the reason I am ill, as I pushed my body relentlessly in demanding careers to earn, earn, earn! Now, I am pouring the little I have left, together with friends help, into getting myself well. That seems right, somehow. I owe myself this healing and I don't think that I have ever put myself first in this way before. Everything seems to be coming together quite easily. The problem is myself believing 100% that I deserve to live and to live well. This is my real challenge. Deciding to go to Mexico feels right in my gut, yet I still feel that there are some adjustments to be made, to make my leaving easier for Josh.

31st January 07: Going away for a full month involves so much preparation. Josh and I talk a little about it every day. Josh has been upset and feeling poorly, having a few days off school. The lows are hard, yet I know we must talk it through, no matter how difficult. My friend Anne is supportive and encouraging through this difficult pending separation. It is sometimes very painful for us both but, as time goes on, I am relieved to see changes in Josh. He is beginning to accept that I am leaving to build up my health: he also is taking an active role in his care while I am away: 'Mum, will my school know that you are away? I would like to stay with Angie, Chris and Robert.'

This way, he feels part of this difficult process, rather than a victim of it. I don't want to leave my beautiful boy in the hands of others and completely let go. Yet I know we both must part from each other this time for our long-term future. We are so fortunate to have such great support all around us: Our friends, Sue Nichols Family Support Centre, staff of Waddesdon School and our local church.

I have an appointment to see the assistant head, his form teacher and matron of Josh's school. As Josh has not been with Waddesdon Secondary School for very long, we know his teachers mostly by sight only. I meet Josh at the school reception area, joining all three people concerned in a private room off reception. I start off by explaining where I am going and why. I ask Josh if he can explain what he believes will be happening in Mexico and he shocks me by saying: 'Well, at least they are not going to carve you up this time mum'. He is very upset. It takes every ounce of my being to contain myself at this point and let Josh have his 'heartbreaking' tears.

After Josh leaves us alone for a while, I briefly explain how we have coped as a family through Cancer over the past few years. I am concerned that Josh may internalise his feelings while I am away and become ill. I find his teachers hugely supportive and reassuring about Josh's care while I am gone. A great weight lifts from my shoulders as I leave the school, which I had not expected. Now I realise that I have underestimated the weight of my decision to go to Issels without Josh.

9th February 07: I have one last CT Scan to bring with me to Mexico. Lying on the machine, I explain my fear of needles to the nurse. It can be difficult to find a vein in my overused arm. A more experienced nurse tries three times with no success. I suggest that she finds a doctor before the numerous attempts start to distress me. A doctor arrives, quite good looking, in his early forties, I think, or perhaps in his late thirties. I wouldn't wish to dent that ego. I don't know his name. He looks at my arm. He then chats to the nurses who start fussing, not taking their eyes off him. Apparently, he has just been watching the cricket. After spending ten minutes feeling my arm for a suitable vein, he successfully inserts the needle. I am relieved and grateful. He says nothing and leaves. From the moment he entered the room to the moment he left, about fifteen minutes in total, he did not acknowledge me, apart from a short smile. I imagine that my arm 'might' feature in his memory. I feel as if I am merely another procedure, nothing more – certainly not a person. This experience could have been so different so very easily leaving me feeling quite different.

10th February 07: It never ceases to amaze me how unexpected things happen. Yet when I look back, I can see how 'it was all meant to happen that way!'

My kind friend, Simon, sends me a newspaper article today claiming amazing life assurance claims for Cancer patients. I have long given up the notion of getting Life Assurance with my type of Cancer. Whilst this was all I thought about when I was initially diagnosed, I have now moved on and this is no longer a big issue for me. However, I think that I will follow this up, as some life assurance will be helpful whenever I do die. After all, I do not have a home to leave in my will any longer. This leads to a discussion with the insurance broker concerned and completion of a lengthy application form, cautiously selecting a fixed-term assurance of fifteen years. I do not urge anyone with Cancer or any chronic long-term life-threatening illness to do this before they feel emotionally strong enough.

13th February 07: I recall when I was heavily pregnant with Josh twelve years ago having my legs and bikini line waxed in preparation, even though I could not even see my bikini line at this late stage! Well, the same applies now for my trip to the Issels Clinic. Well why not! You have to prepare yourself and feel in the mood. What's more, I will be giving birth to myself when I am there! No, I am not going mad. At least, I don't think so, anyway.

The next day I receive a thoughtful call from my oncologist. The insurance company has asked her for a report on my condition. This was expected, but I did not expect her to call me. It is considerate of her and I appreciate her thoughtfulness. We discuss what I have said and she suggests the comments she can add. I am then shocked by what follows. She mentions that *when* Herceptin stops working, there are several other treatment options I can try! I am stunned, and plummet for about ten days after this revelation. This lady certainly does not deal in hope but, instead, I believe she tries to handle me gently in case I live up to the indictment (on my file) of 'anxious and emotional patient!' No doubt, this will follow me everywhere through the healthcare system. I cannot help but express my emotions exactly as I feel them, right in front of her or any other doctors/nurses, for that matter. It is clear that my Cancer is life-threatening as my oncologist constantly looks for signs of any further tumours that may be lurking somewhere, as she investigates every inch of my body thoroughly on some appointments. If this had happened two years ago, I would be in a state of panic and desperation. I can 'hear' what she is saying and coming to realise that Cancer treatment in this country is one-dimensional – in that it can only try to attack the Cancer 'visible' in my body. But, as I understand from what I have read, a malignant tumour can take up to ten years to develop. So whilst traditional medical treatment works at removing and killing the 'visible' cancer, what can be done pro-actively to bolster my immune system so that further cancers cannot develop? My hardest efforts are not in 'fighting Cancer', as I hear often from other patients, but in refusing to accept that this is all there is!

20

Hope and Separation

What about hope! What about my own spirit! What about my quality of life! What about my poor, neglected immune system! But I have never been one to take the conventional route. Having experienced how well I felt when I was receiving Simi's treatments, I want more of these treatments. How I wish that our current health system could offer patients complementary healing therapies too? I do not feel that optimum health and well-being can truly be attained with treatment of disease/illness as an entity separate to the person, involving only physical form and dismissing mind and spirit.

I have found our medical profession for the most part 'detached' when it comes to caring for patients. This is not to say that there are some wonderful, dedicated professionals within the system, such as the wonderful Sister, Jackie Benson, of the Day Surgery unit, whose behaviour stood out for her level of 'care and compassion' far and above the required practicalities of her role and with my current oncologist, who dares to take the time to build a personal relationship with me.

The detached attitude and behaviour makes the whole 'patient experience' much more stressful than it needs to be and impedes healing. Since my diagnosis I have been 'treated' for the most part, and 'nothing more' until I asked for a second opinion. Healing takes place within the patient themselves, involving mind, body and spirit. The essential and often missing link between treatment (by medical staff) and healing (within the patient) is CARE. It is not tangible, it cannot be statistically proven, it is a feeling of being 'cared for', understood and respected. Whilst breast care nurses currently provide vital care and a compassionate, listening ear, Cancer specialists and consultants are often too busy and detached to do so, leaving the patient in sudden limbo burdened with devastating information etc. I feel that Care needs to be a seamless, continuous stream flowing throughout the patient's experience of Cancer: flowing from diagnosis, through chemotherapy, radiotherapy and follow-up appointments. Perhaps this is a lot to ask, but it can be done and is sometimes already happening. As a former Cancer patient recently commented: 'Our healthcare system does show care and compassion but, unfortunately, it comes at the end of your life when you go to a hospice. There the care is wonderful.' It does not involve more resources, just a little more time and empathy on the part of all medical staff, leading to empowered patient experience and greater sense of well-being. Here are my suggestions based on my experience so far:

Putting 'Heart' into the NHS
(Small changes, few resources, huge benefits.)

a) Medical Staff to take time to build relationships with their patients

b) All medical staff to treat patients as people and not as procedures

c) Doctors on hospital ward rounds to introduce themselves by name

d) Doctors to come on their rounds in smaller numbers, so as not to intimidate the patients they are supposed to be empowering.

e) Doctors to sit down beside hospital beds when talking to patients, rather than towering over the patient's feet at the far end.

f) Doctors explain the jargon they use to patients, e.g., 'Your Cancer is stage 2'.

g) Doctors to pay attention to patients' feelings, not just symptoms and surgery results.

h) Radiographers to allow patients to choose from a choice of music or bring in their own favourite CD to be played while they are having radiotherapy.

i) Nurses to take time to explain hospital procedures to a patient. (A leaflet is not enough)

j)   Doctors to talk to patients gently before they go for surgery, so as to make them feel at ease and relaxed! (not upset and panicked)

k)   The surgeon to meet the patient in the pre-op room before surgery. This can be very reassuring. (Mind you, this depends on the surgeon!)

l)   All medical staff to acknowledge patients in corridors and waiting rooms with a cheerful smile and greeting, rather than ignoring patients until they are called in for their appointment. We are people/patients the minute we enter hospital!

m)   Cancer patients to see the same oncologist on a regular basis, building strong relationships throughout their cancer journey, contributing to their sense of well-being.

n)   Light music to be played gently in the background in the chemo suite, aiding relaxation in the often fast-paced, intense atmosphere.

o)   Volunteers to bring tea/coffee round to patients on chemo suite and take time to chat to patients.

p)   Missionary support to be available to Cancer patients on the chemo suite when they are having gruelling treatment.

15th February 07: This morning Josh and I have an appointment with the family therapist to put support in place, in case Josh needs additional emotional help while I am away. Josh is comfortable coming here: and at some level, he realises that this is all extra help for him while I am here and away. We have a good discussion. Jan, the family therapist points out that it will be good for Josh to see that he can manage without me. I find this hard to absorb but know that there is a grain of truth in it somewhere. Regardless of how others may view my trip to Mexico, I see it as really positive for us both. I feel excited and am looking forward to it. I am not going to Mexico because all else has failed and my case is desperate. I am going now because I know that wholistic treatment in every sense of the word will give me the best chance of healing. I am going to give birth to my suppressed self, which in turn, can only benefit us both in the long-term.

18th February 07: This evening, Josh and I are so aware that this is our last night before we part for a whole month. We have prepared for this – talked about it, cried about it and felt our way through our feelings every step of the way. However there is no denying that these last twenty-four hours are the most difficult. Josh goes to bed as usual at nine in the evening, but ten minutes later, he comes back downstairs, as he cannot sleep. I am not surprised. I then take him up to my bed and we cuddle for a long time. We both sleep fitfully that night.

I have a strange dream – I feel that my chest wall, where I have had my breast removed, is broken or crushed, leaving a very red, pulsating heart exposed. I feel so vulnerable. Leaving my beautiful boy for a whole month is possibly the most difficult thing I have ever done. My heart breaks if I think too long and hard about what we are doing.

The following day we get up as usual: this morning is a school day, but we know all too well that everything is completely different. Josh sits down to eat breakfast; tears quietly pouring down his beautiful face. We cuddle and I try to reassure him: 'Darling, we will both be fine. We are both going to have great adventures.' He leaves for school through the back door this time and I wave him off as happily as I can. I then go indoors and pour my eyes out. Five minutes later, the front doorbell rings and there he is, tears flowing down his face. We hug and hold each other, clutching on to all the reassurances in the world. He finally leaves. I close the front door this time and sink to the floor in tears. I telephone his school and remind his teacher that today I am leaving and that Josh is very upset. They reassure me that they will be there to support him. I have to let go now. I have to.

Up to this point all my attention has been devoted to making sure that Josh has all the support he needs: from his teachers and matron at school, our local doctor, Sue Nichols Family Support Centre and friends. And now it is time for me. Imagery comes to mind of a large ship ready to leave on its maiden voyage, with its anchor raised, steadily loosening each one of the ropes securing it. It is now almost ready to set sail. Only a few more ropes to loosen and we are off!

My angel friend Auriel kindly picks me up to go to the airport. My mind is swamped with my little boy's sadness and amazing courage. Conversation fails me. Waving bye-bye to Auriel, my face attempting a tense smile, I enter Departures scarcely ready for the weeks ahead. To my relief, I quickly meet up with my guiding angel Claire, who is coming with me. I shall always remember how fate guided us together for this healing journey.

Going back only a couple of weeks, I text Claire: 'Hi Claire, do you fancy a free trip to Mexico?' to which Claire quickly replied: 'Have you won a holiday love?' Containing my surprise, I replied: 'No, I am going off to a Cancer Clinic for a month'. Then, to my amazement, Claire replied: 'Yes, I can come with you for two weeks if that is helpful.' Not really believing this, I sent a return text: 'That would be brilliant but perhaps talk it over with your husband first and let's talk later.' And guess what? Claire emailed me later that same evening saying that would be fine: the wonderful thing about her agreement to come with me was that she did not need to know anything about where we were going, hence no additional pressure for me. I was gob-smacked. What a friend! I feel so very fortunate. In retrospect, I am glad that I did not attempt to go alone, although I would have done so. As Claire is a friend it works out better in many ways, as I can really consider myself rather than be concerned about how a 'partner' is coping with this.

We check in and go through to Departures. As we wait in the departure lounge, I text Josh. We had agreed that I would let him know when I was about to board the plane. A little while later I receive a beautiful text back from him, saying simply: 'Bye', with a smiley face. What an amazing boy! I am so relieved that he could do this. I am so proud of him. I learned later that Josh had been in tears for most of that day, which only shows an amazing strength and selflessness for one so young. Finally, this ship has now set sail on its maiden voyage to a new life.

Claire and I check-in and go through passport control and security – an ordeal in itself, only to be told that the flight is delayed for the next three hours. However, we are served refreshments and have lots to chat about, as we never have had an opportunity to be together like this before. We eventually board the plane and I am relieved to discover that we have spare seats next to us giving us ample opportunity to really rest, if not sleep, on this long flight. I am a bit concerned about my energy levels, with such a huge time difference. We have a lovely trip. We both watch 'The Queen' film, which we have not seen before, have dinner and then I actually get some sleep!

20th February 07: We arrive late into Chicago, resulting in missing our connecting flight to San Diego. Before checking-in again for a later flight, I have one of my 'impulsive' urges! I approach a ground attendant and ask him if he has any idea of how much it will cost us to get a taxi to San Diego. I do not really want to have to stay locally and fly out again tomorrow. He smiles and, cupping my face in his warm hands, replies: 'Now, pet, it will take you about eight hours by taxi to San Diego, which will cost you a small fortune'. At this stage, I have completely lost track of time, what with the time difference and the three-hour delay. I also do not have a strong sense of where we actually are. But it is starting to slowly dawn on me. So we give in and book into a local hotel, flying out again later the next day. Once we check into the hotel, we dump our luggage in our room, deciding to let go of our frustration at having to stop over. We decide to make the most of this time together and so head to the bar! Where else? We may be going to a Cancer Clinic but we can certainly enjoy ourselves on the way! We both give up trying to figure out what time it is here and what time it is at home. Happily exhausted, I decide to have my last drink here. Hours later, the bar staff indicate, not so subtly, that they are closing. On the way to our room, Claire enlightens me that it must be about five in the morning, English time. Gosh, we have been up for absolute hours. I am very pleased with myself.

This relaxation time is precious, giving me time to let go of home and re-orientate myself towards my challenging experience ahead. I have had little, if any, time to consider what I am about to experience at Issels before I left home. I just know that I have to come to Issels for my complete healing.

21st February 07: After sleeping really well, we awake quite refreshed and board our late departure the following day to San Diego. Nearly there now. Upon arriving in San Diego, we look out for the Issels Representative meeting us with a sign with my name on it. Claire finds him and we are now on our way to Issels. At long last, I am nearly there! We pass through the Mexican border quietly, arriving at the Oasis of Hope Hospital in the dark. We are shown to our room in the Issels Clinic on the fifth floor. I feel very strange being here. I have looked forward to being here for so long and now here I am. Gosh, now what? I don't know what to expect and that fills me with dread. I do know I want it, whatever this experience brings.

21

Salvation

I have left the professional hands of a beleaguered, distant and often-cold health service system back in England, I feel battered, bruised and somewhat disillusioned by the relentless series of surgeries, scans, tests and treatments that I have undergone for over three years, with little hope. I am not at ease with having Cancer-attacking chemicals alone in my body although I do know that this has been very necessary. I feel in my bones that I need more help than this to heal. I know that I am about to embark on a very spiritual journey, taking me back into the womb, so to speak. In a way, this is my second chance for life

Nothing prepared me for the amazing atmosphere of the Issels Treatment Centre at The Oasis of Hope Hospital: the genuinely caring, attentive staff and highly skilled, professional, human, approachable doctors, not to mention the smiling faces of the remarkable patients, many of whom have been inwardly guided to this 'healing' oasis. Occupying the fifth floor of this private hospital, the Issels Treatment Centre provides integrative immunotherapy treatment as developed by Dr Josef Issels, a world renowned pioneer of interactive Cancer medicine for over 40 years – a comprehensive service including a twenty-eight day stay at the hospital followed up by a six-month home vaccine pack and overnight stay every six months over a five-year period.[8]

Here I am clearly treated as Jacinta – a person first and foremost, who happens to have Breast Cancer. I have a room on a floor devoted to seriously ill Cancer patients and their carers/partners. There is a team of up to six medically qualified,

---

[8] Full details of the Issels treatment regime and additional information can be found at Appendix G at the end of this book.

friendly doctors, three or four of whom are available all day, and twenty-four hour nursing care. I quickly notice the meticulous attention to each patient's treatment, with constant tailoring and fine-tuning day-by-day. All of the staff, whether doctor, nurse, catering staff, cleaner, receptionist, administrator or missionary, smile with their hearts. Everyone in this hospital is warm, friendly and approachable, no matter what time of day.

Josh's emails are like a lifeline for me. I miss him so much already and long to hear from him.

From: Josh
Sent: 21st February 2007 18.12
Hi can you tell me when you thought about going to Mexico, for my homework, please. How are you doing? Are you enjoying your stay ,i am missing you alot but I am enjoying my stay here. I have been getting so much homework lately but i wont let it get on top of me. We are having bella pizza tonight !!!!!!!!!!!!!!!!! and if you dont get this today the date is 21/2/07.

22nd February 07: I have a jumpy start. The full impact of leaving my son for a whole month, jet lag due to flight delay and missed connections, too little time to become accustomed to new surroundings, new doctors and new treatment hits me with a mighty force, triggering my primal fears. As a result, when a male nurse attempts to give me a liver injection in my bottom this morning, I panic and almost hit the poor soul. Later this morning, a doctor comes to withdraw thirteen vials of blood.[9] He looks kind and caring. Surprisingly this does not hurt at all. Next my vital signs are monitored. There is a lot happening all at once. Writing an email to Josh slows down everything for me and helps me find my feet for a moment.

---

[9] http://www.issels.com/TreatmentSummary.aspx

From: Mum

Date: Thu, 22 Feb 2007 01:34:

Hello Darling

I am thrilled to hear your news. Lucky you having such a great time at Angies – gooey chocolate pancakes and bella pizza!!!!

The time here is ten past five in the afternoon and we are going downstairs now for a very healthy dinner. We have just had one full day here today, as we did not get here until ten last night. We missed the flight from Chicago and had to stay an extra night in Chicago and it was snowy there.

Your homework sounds interesting. I hope this info helps you. I first thought of going to Mexico probably in October just gone. I am being very well looked after. This morning Claire and I walked five minutes down to the sea and walked along the beach. The weather is good here, warm and sunny but chilly in the evening. I am feeling better already and can't wait to come home to you with lots of energy and then we can play rough and tumble like we used to do.

You will be fine with your homework, pet, as you always plan it very well. There is a little envelope on its way to you. Let me know when you get it.

I have your picture beside my bed and I am sending you loving hugs while you sleep.

Love mum xx

23rd February 07: Today I feel terribly nervous and frightened going down to theatre to have a line fitted in my chest. Claire cannot console me, although if she had not been there I dread to think what would have happened! On our way down in the lift, a male nurse advises me to calm down. These are the worst words I can hear when I am terrified. For a moment I am reminded of the detached healthcare back home. I bite his nose off: 'I can't calm down just because you tell me to. I don't work like that!' At which point, he disappears never to be seen again that day: yet another poor soul bites the dust. Then, as I am being prepared for theatre, I start telling the surgeon that I am going to have my baby. Poor man, he must think that I have lost it. In my mind, I am going to give birth to my 'little' self – the part of me, suppressed for most of my life. I know what I mean, but it is difficult for anyone else to understand at this shaky stage.

'Little Me'

I am NOT ready to let all my creativity out here and now.
I have been hanging on your cross
for a very long time
not 'dead' but suffering
I have now put down this cross
and walking towards the light.
Daddy I saw you carry your cross all your life
you never put it down
Oh how I wish that you had
then perhaps I would have known 'you'
You were precious to me but never there
You hurt me deeply
I do not want to follow you any more
and carry the cross you gave me
The 'little child' in me wants to live
Free of suffering, free of guilt
That never belonged to me
Deep down under the ground
Forgotten, alone yet 'alive'
Digging my way out with every ounce of my being
A treasure chest
Packed full of rich, precious gems
Open and spilling out
So many broken hearts
Rich red, warm and pulsating
Alive, breathing, relieved
Is it safe to be 'me?

I wake up later in my bed and the line is fitted, thank goodness. I am a little stiff and sore but relieved. My heart lifts as I read Josh's emails over the next few days:

From: Josh
Sent: 23rd February 2007 18.22
hello

thanks for replying but they are not called credits, they are called merits. does the beach have sand?

i am doing my homework now so i will have to go, how are you ?

From: Mum
Date: Sat, 24 Feb 2007 02:30:
Hi Darling

Well done you for getting through all your homework this week. I am sorry that I got the words muddled up with credit and merit. Mum is always doing something like that. The beach here is very sandy and long but there are no children about at all. So you are not missing much pet. I am thrilled to hear that you have spoken up about how you would like to spend your weekend. Have a lot fun this weekend cos you deserve it after working so hard this week. I have sent you another envelope pet so let me know when you get something. By the way, have you got taller yet?

Talk soon

Love you to bits and back again xxxx

From: Josh
Sent: 24th February 2007 10.39
Hi

i got the envelope i will keep the heart in a safe place. i don't think i have got much taller yet.

I am going to have my cerial now, talk soon.

From: Mum
Date: 25 Feb 2007 02:56
Hi Bigger Boy

I am glad you got the envelope with my heart in it. Take good care of my heart pet. I hear that you are spending part of the weekend with Martin and part with Chris and Robert, let me know if you went home to Martin's or to Kiki's. Have you had a good time? We went to a little resort today with other patients to a little village called Rosarito. I bought you a special something for your neck which I know you will love. I am posting another envelope to you tonight. It was sunny tonight but very cold as well.

with love from me and lots of hugs and kisses xxxxxxx

From: Josh
Sent: 25 February 2007 18.33
Hello
i have just arrived back from kiki's, i had a brilliant time. i got some new yu-gi-oh cards! how are you?
hugs xxxxxxxxxxxxxxxx

Having been here almost a week now, I am beginning to fall into a routine of sorts. A typical day consists of:
Morning Prayers
Vital signs checked, including blood pressure, pulse, temperature, weight and body mass
Visit by 1 – 3 doctors
Ozone, B17/Laetrile, Vitamin C, Protein infusions
Optional lectures
40 + supplements
9 –13 glasses of veg/fruit juice
3 organic meals
Evening movie/talk/prayers and sing-songs
Vaccines, I believe, come later.
I am slowly overcoming my anxiety and responding to treatment, due to the caring, respectful, loving manner in which I am treated as a person. I receive all my treatments in my bedroom, which is a treat in itself. I feel more like an invited guest than a vulnerable patient.

26th February 07: Towards the end of my first week, I wake up in the middle of the night, feeling so small and vulnerable, crying quietly in bed. Claire wakes up and sits with me while I sob. I feel small and terrified of everything. In the early hours as darkness begrudgingly gives way to light, I anxiously express my feelings:

A Wicked Day

A wicked day
Born of hate and self-loathing
An evil sky
Bearing down so low
Heavy hearts
Broken into pieces
Blood running cold
As if you'd know
Hidden neath a smile
Locked in darkness
Starved of light
A gentle beauty
A tender soul
A breath of light
for you to know

27th February 07: I wake up determined to go to prayers at eight in the morning. During prayers Marsha and Dottie - missionaries, ask us to close our eyes and take ourselves to a place where we feel safe and can be with God. I find my special woods, with the light shining through the trees. Jesus is here. 'Is there anything you would like to say to God?' Marsha asks. Within minutes, an overwhelming feeling surges up from the pit of my stomach. I try to resist but my feelings overtake me.

'Where was God when I was locked away in the cellar, naked and tiny?' Then I cry and cry and cry, from a part of me that has never cried before. Vicky holds me close as my abandoned, ashamed little child pours out her shame in the safe, loving arms of this wonderful oasis. I now realise that this part of me has probably never even 'lived' before. I am surrounded by so much love and feel safe. I have come home and know I will heal here. I feel exhilarated and very much alive.

During prayers this evening, I share the story about selling our home, feeling empowered through my treatments and feeling excited and full of fun. I have woken up and now see with clear, open eyes. Everything is beautiful.

Back in our room, I open my laptop and rapidly key in my thoughts and feelings after my amazing experience earlier today. I want to share this with everyone tomorrow morning in prayers. In the meantime, one of the nurses pops in and I ask her for some pain-relief to help me sleep more easily with the discomfort of my fitted line. In the meantime, Claire and I set off to find a printer somewhere in the hospital, to print my thoughts. We are shown to a small office and busily print off about 10 copies. We arrive back to our room twenty minutes later to find another nurse panicking, in Spanish, about my pain relief. Thank goodness I know some Spanish. She blurts out that she cannot find me and knowing I am in pain, she is very worried that something has happened. She looks very confused to learn that I have been busy printing – of all things. All three of us fall about laughing.

From: Mum
Date: Mon, 27 Feb 2007 03:52
Hi Pet

I am so thrilled that you had a great time at Kiki's and even MORE yugio cards! Who is a very very lucky boy. I bet Kiki really loved seeing you and really looked after you.

Today Claire and I changed rooms and now we have more space and are cosier. When you have time, do you think that you could draw me a picture for our book of the outline of a woman (just the frame from head to foot) with an outline of a smaller woman inside of her with her head as high as her neck.

Each day Josh I drink many glasses of fresh vegetable and fruit juices with lots of vitamins in them. The doctors check me every day and have told me that I am doing really well and getting much stronger. I hope you are ready for a lot of rough and tumble when I get home.

Have a really good week at school. I will be looking forward to hearing all you have been doing.

Love from mum and oodles of hugs.xxxxxxxxxxxxxxx

From: Josh
Sent: 27 February 2007 15.49
Hi

could you describe the picture for me again ,but i might not be able to draw it cos i have lots of homework. In the picture do you want the outline of the lady to have arms and legs? do the doctors speak in english at the hospital?

I need to go now bye bye.

From: mum
Date: 27 Feb 2007 21:18
Hi Darling

Only do my picture if you feel like it otherwise don't worry about it. I am trying to picture a person growing within a person. It is important that you do your homework and have lots of fun when you have time. You are doing so well keeping on top of your homework. I am so proud of you. The picture is the outline only of a woman with arms and legs facing you and inside this outline/frame is another outline of a smaller woman exactly the same but not as tall (only up the neck of the first woman). Yes the doctors all here speak a mixture of English and Spanish so I can understand them. They are all very very friendly and nice. Today they cleaned my blood so I am feeling good. Claire has gone down to the cafe to get some lunch for me while I email you.

Love you pet xxxxxxxxx

28th February 07: This is going to be an amazing day. I wake up excited and a little anxious. I feel it is so important that I go to prayers and read out my special healing over the past two days. I meet Bruce on the landing outside my room. When he notices the wad of papers in my hand – all ten copies, he comments: 'Your talk is not that long, is it?' Poor man. I think he thought I was going to talk forever! What, me? Claire and I sit beside Don, another patient, and we all sing together. Bruce then invites me up to speak. How strange yet comfortable this is, sitting in front of these beautiful, courageous people talking about what's in my heart. I read out the following:

'I wake up feeling tall and energised this morning. I get ready slowly for breakfast. I shower carefully, choose what to wear, taking a pride in how I look, although a little weary after getting ready. I have plans today. I want to have a good breakfast in preparation for treatment later, especially the vaccine. Later in the morning, while having my ozone and B17 infusions, I notice Dottie and Marsha 'hovering' (angels 'hover' you know!) out on the landing. I welcome them in. Then Marsha asks me tentatively if we can pray for anything that happened in the past. All of a sudden, out of nowhere, the floodgates open yet again and I sob uncontrollably. I do not want to have to go back to that awful place (the cellar) ever again. Marsha and Dottie and Claire then come round my bed and holding my hands with love, we pray. I then have an amazing experience:

I can see myself hunched up naked in a corner of the cold damp cellar and then as we pray, I slowly get up and walk out of the cellar, unashamedly, upstairs to the landing of our home. My father is standing there. I stand in front of him, asking: 'Why did you do this?' He does not answer. Next to him, God is standing with his open arms, welcoming me. As I look up at him, I grow taller and taller. His eyes exude warmth, compassion and an amazing love that I have never felt before, in our home or ever in my life. Beside him, water cascades down, purging me of all my pain, flowing away down the winding staircase. I go to daddy and hug him without fear. Taking his hand, I guide him to the cascading water. He takes a couple of steps but stops. I let go and purge myself some more. I pick up my clothes and confidently walk down the long, winding, mahogany staircase without looking back. I open the heavy, iron front door and slam it firmly behind me, with a strength I didn't know I had. With a new determination, I stride down the middle of the road towards the harbour at the bottom. At the water's edge, I look up to the sky and fly off with strength and purpose. I am free. Lack of love has been my cancer but with the love of God and everyone here, I am being healed.'

The oddest thing about writing these pages is that I had the good news earlier today that my lungs are clear, yet I have not even thought to mention that fact when writing this! I realise now that this almost miraculous purging of my shame and guilt from my father's incest has been the chemotherapy that I really needed all this time. Thank God I did not wait any longer.

While I am not a very vocal person when it comes to religion, I definitely know that something is going on here between God and I. This feeling follows me around, becoming quite funny at times.

Claire and I ask the missionaries if they have any DVDs we can borrow. Fortunately they have quite a collection. After some searching, I find one called 'The Perfect Stranger', which grabs my attention – a sort of thriller, I think, which I love. Claire and I agree and tuck ourselves up in bed comfortably later to watch this movie. I cannot believe what this film is about – a meeting between a professional wife and mother in her late thirties and a man in his early forties who is none other than 'Jesus'! Here he is again! The entire film takes place at a restaurant dining table over dinner and involves a long discussion. I cannot believe my eyes or my ears. How did I manage to choose this? Jesus is all around me. I know it.

I hear from my darling boy this evening and my heart goes out to him. I know what I am doing is worth it.

From: Josh

Sent: 28 February 2007 19.44
Hello
i got the postcard you sent me from chicago. in the picture can i draw the back of a woman instead of the front? we walked the dogs today ,angie said that if i get upset we can go out and walk the dogs.
lots of hugs!!!!!!!!!!!!!!!!!!!!!!

From: Mum
Date: 01 March 2007 19.26pm
Hi Josh xx kisses
How are you doing pet? Is it getting a bit difficult for you? I know you miss mummy and I miss you pet. But do you know what would make me the happiest person in the world? You having lots and lots of fun while I am away. Do not worry about me pet. Just have lots and lots of fun. The time will go faster if you play lots.
I have sent you another special envelope yesterday which you should get in the next four days.
Have you received more envelopes since the last one?
Love you darling (heart)

I am so blessed and feel so relieved to have so many wonderful friends looking out for my boy, especially Angie and her family
3 March'07 I sense from Josh's email today that any change is unsettling for him. I also feel that it is still too early and too difficult for Josh and I to speak on the telephone yet. Perhaps in my third week, when I am closer to coming home.

From: Josh
Sent: 3 March 2007 18.05pm

Hi mum

the presents are fine. i am staying at angies over the week end. i am not sure about going to auriels .you can ring me if you want but i am ok emailing.

bye

4th March 07: Today is strange without my buddy Claire. I walk the beach alone, lost in thought. I know that I need this 'alone' time too. In fact, I have also needed the rest since Claire has gone, as we just kept chatting and laughing. Now, I begin to feel recharged and – guess what? I start dancing in my room and feel great! There is definitely a whole lot of healing going on here.

The next day, I get up and go to prayers. I feel my cancer is going due to my spiritual healing. We all sing 'The Old Rugged Cross' this morning and the following verse keeps reverberating in my ears:

'I cling to the old rugged cross
And exchange it one day for a crown'

All I can sing is:

'I carry the old rugged cross
And exchange today for a crown'

I feel that I have come home to Jesus and to myself. I feel 'reborn'. I do not need to know all the ins and outs of my treatment here. I accept and trust it is doing me good. My initial criticisms on arrival, about essentially cosmetic elements, were masking my fear of the unknown, taking me back to my childhood and my mother's changing moods. Now, I no longer need to know. Believe me, this is a glorious feeling and a great relief[10].

---

[10] For more information on my amazing journey of healing at Issels, see my website www.cancershiddengifts.co.uk

6th March 07: Today is hard. I feel lonely all day. I go to withdraw some money from the cash machine nearby, but become stressed and overwhelmed, trying to convert the currency from pesos to dollars and then to sterling. I walk to the dentist on my own, feeling alone and weepy. It's quite an achievement for me to go to the dentist by myself; with a need for complex dental work involving tooth extraction, replacement of amalgam with white filling in another tooth and clearing of infection under my gum and all under sedation. My needle phobia has always made these trips traumatic, shaking my little world. However this experience at the dentist's goes very well. I know that I am in good hands. It is so lovely that the doctors and staff here are concerned and monitor me closely. Dr. Lagos kindly walks me back to the hospital, as I feel a bit woozy after the sedation, although I am not in pain. However a few hours later I feel very cold and start shivering. Shock is starting to grab hold of me. Josh's loving email later warms my heart.

From: 'Josh
Date: 6 May 2007 18.48pm
Hi Mum

we have received the envelope for chris and robert but it got damaged in the post and the bracelets were lost in the post. my tummy is better now and at school today i made beans on toast. i received the letter with the necklace in and i will try and send a picture of it later. At school today i got my bottle opener that i made in class but i will leave it in the packaging until you get back. it was a full eclipse. i have my own rabbit now but it will stay here, its name is trecool. lots of hugs

7th March 07: I am now half way through my stay here at Issels. I am responding well to this treatment, as I knew I would before I came. Thank god I had the bottle to come. I have been listening to a Paul McKenna Relaxation tape this morning and the words: 'Be aware of your attachment to suffering and release that attachment'. These words ring loud in my ears: even though I have listened to this tape many times before, I have never really heard those words. Perhaps I couldn't hear them at home, but here I can. Since coming to Issels, I have completely broken free of suffering's heavy chains and now stand alone, fully empowered and free. My healing is complete. Cancer is no longer needed in my life. Thank you Jesus for helping me to listen to you and act upon your words.

A young patient dies today but even such a sad passing seems somehow uplifting. Surrounded by so much love and support, this young patient gently leaves this world in God's hands. I notice that some patients come here when it is too late, and I wonder if they come here out of desperation. I feel that complete belief in this treatment is paramount to the healing process.

The following morning, I receive a very upsetting email from Josh:

From: 'Josh
Date: Tue, 07 Mar 2007 19.42pm
Hi
i am not sure if i am going to enjoy staying with simon and i dont know where i go on thursday. i was pulled out of class today because i was crying cos i was missing you.
Love Josh

I knew Josh was struggling but have been trying not to worry. All three doctors come in to see me and look at me so lovingly, really concerned as I cry. One of these gentle souls suggests that I fly Josh out to be with me and they will collect him from the airport. I consider this for a few minutes but know this is not the answer but instead only a very temporary fix. After some careful consideration, I tentatively call Angie and check how Josh is whilst calming myself down. I speak to my little boy so far, far away. It is so good to hear his voice but I can tell that we are both trying to be strong here. Keeping everything upbeat, our chat cheers us both up. As I am more than half way through my treatment, we can start talking on the telephone regularly.

Speaking before this would have been too much to bear for either of us.

Later today, Bruce, Vicky and I walk along the beach and amazingly they warmly invite Josh and I to stay with them when I come back, hopefully in October. How lovely is that! More love!

Bruce and Vicky provide a precious volunteer ministry 'Project Oasis of Hope' to patients and their families at Issels and Oasis of Hope.[11] Their endless love, encouragement and selfless support strengthens and inspires the many courageous souls who are fortunate to find this healthy Oasis.

Today is also Woman's day in Mexico. What a lovely celebration! I also gave myself my first enema today, lying on my bed. Confident, eh! I feel more and more an integral part of this place and so at ease. I can be myself here with all my aches and pains. Yet I have never laughed so much. I am at last so lovingly treated, supported and accepted by those who are treating me. I am amazed at how I do not see us all here as cancer patients. I do not feel we are ill. Sometimes I wonder if it is the British health system itself that is sick. We are all treated here as the unique, wonderful individuals we are, who happen to have cancer but also have the courage to follow this course of treatment, with a strong will to survive and get really well mentally, physically and emotionally. I guess this is a manifestation of the true ethos of Issels.

Three years and over one hundred appointments, treatments and procedures later. I have found what I have needed to truly heal – treatment for 'all of me'.[12]

10th March 07: The days are going very slowly at the moment and I feel sad and somewhat removed. I know that I have a hurdle from my past to cross this week when it comes to my having my Coley's vaccine. 'A part of me died that day, as a child, the part of me that didn't know how to live'. The prospect of having the Coley's vaccine fills me with dread.

---

[11] See appendix H at the end of this book
[12] See appendix I at the end of this book.

Please God help me cope with all these needles.
Josh's emails give me unlimited strength:

From: 'Josh
Date: 11 March 2007 20.28pm
Hi Mum
I had a nice time at Martins and i got more yu-gi-oh cards! i have been counting down the days for a while now.
Bye

12th March 07: Today I wake up dancing! Amazing that I can do this, considering that I am having my first Coley's vaccine later. I receive a lovely email from Josh, which delights my soul and sets me up for the day.

From: Josh
Date: 12 March 2007 20.42pm
HI the pics look really good but who was the person in number 14 and what is that plaster on your chest? its not long till you come home. on tuesday i will be making beef burgers at school and i will be able to cook them at home. how are you? i recieved the letter with the £5 in, are any more letters coming my way? there will be a letter coming to you in the post soon.
Bye huuuuuuuuuuuuuuggggggggggggggggggssss

My fear of needles has become very obvious to staff early on in my treatment. The doctors' reactions to my fear here surprise me. They immediately suggest that they put some Emla cream on my skin beforehand, then an ice-pack to numb the area further, followed by a small injection of Lithocane to ensure the area is very numb hence reducing the trauma for me. I instantly relax as I can see that they respect my fear. Their concern outweighs the importance of accomplishing the procedure. The love that doctors show me eases my distress. I can even envisage overcoming my fear completely with time.

At prayers this morning, I feel that my 'broken heart' has healed. I have no argument with anyone anywhere about anything. I just feel full of love. My problem has never been fearing death. Sadly, I have been afraid of life. I did not know how to 'live!'

From: Mum
Date: 14 Mar 2007 06:38
Hi Pet It was great talking to you this morning. You certainly have had lots going on. Angie sent me some photos of you – the cook! I am impressed. I shall expect you to cook all meals from now on you know pet! Only joking. Look after your toe pet and keep it very clean. Guess what! I have met some friends out here called Bruce and Vicky. They are missionaries at the hospital here. They have invited us to stay with them later this summer if we want to. Their place overlooks the long beach and Bruce says that he would like to sleep out in the open with you on the balcony one night. Sounds good eh! I have sent one last envelope with a surprise in it. I really liked your very long email. Well done pet. Love you lots and sending you hugsssssssssssssssssssss xxxxxxxxxxxxxxxxxxxxxxxxx

From: 'Josh
Date: 14 March 2007 20.12pm
hello
it is less than a week to go!!!!!!!!!!!! when you get back i will be able to cook beans on toast, beef burgers and scones! i am looking forward to the envelope. tell me when yours arrives. how are you? have i mentioned that chris slit his wrist on friday ,in art? bye bye

15th March 07: I am beginning to think about going home but at the same time want to make the very most of every single healing moment here.

From: Mum
Date: Thu, 15 Mar 2007 22:30
Gosh what a big heart you have sent me Josh. Mine is even bigger! I will be home on Wednesday at 12.40pm and I can't wait. I am doing so good pet. see you so very soon. mum xxx

From: 'Josh
Date: 16 March 2007 19.38pm
Hi
miss fitzgerald said that she would like to see you when you come back, but not until your ready.
my heart is bigger! bye!

Now in my last week, I am very aware of leaving this wonderful oasis. Whilst I am so looking forward to seeing Josh again after so long, I also feel a little wary of leaving this protected, healing environment where all my needs have been met with love. My life has changed once again and I know that there is no looking back. I am now starting to prepare for going home. This involves saying goodbye to everyone, talking to the doctors regarding my follow up home treatment plan, ordering my six-month supply of supplements and collecting my ice box containing my six month supply of vaccines. Quite a lot to think about. I do feel concerned about flying home alone especially with the box of vaccines and having to change planes at San Francisco. My friend Claire arranged special assistance (in the form of a wheelchair) for me at the airport, enabling me to pass through check-in easier. I am used to flying but not in this vulnerable state.

As my departure day arrives, I wake up very early and finish packing. I only brought one suitcase so packing to go home is proving to be quite a challenge. Vicky and Bruce come in to find me on my hands and knees squeezing even more clothes into my bulging suitcase while flinging endless articles into the bin. What I can't fit, I don't need, or so I believe at this moment. Vicky offers her help suggesting that perhaps a larger case might do the trick. Bruce brings me a spare suitcase and Vicky sorts out my mess, while I continue flapping about. I often don't realise that I need help. So many years of fending for myself, I never really developed the habit of asking for help when I needed it. Of course, I no longer need to do so any more. What a warm and new feeling! I guess I will experience many different feelings now in 'my new life'. My mind is full of goodbyes to all the wonderful patients, doctors, nurses and staff that I have met here. This is very important to me and I want to do this properly, giving it the time it deserves.

I am supposed to pop in to see the dentist for a last check-up before I leave but I cannot see how I will fit this all in. Bruce humorously suggests that Vicky accompany me to the dentist in case I get run over by a car! 'It would be a crying shame to have come this far and then die in a road traffic accident!' In these situations, black humour comes into it's own. This is part and parcel of not merely 'living with' or 'surviving' but really thriving through cancer. In fact, I have never laughed so much as I have done at Issels. I never envisaged for a second that I would have so much fun!

Having said my goodbyes, I want to say a prayer with Bruce and Vicky and the other missionaries before I leave. I want this to be the last thing that I do at Issels. I want to be protected for my long journey home. Bruce and Vicky, Chris and Byron, Jennifer and George encircle me, each saying a special personal prayer. I feel so protected and blessed. What a precious, deeply spiritually healing experience. No other words come to my lips other than: 'Jesus has touched me'. I know deep down, I am healed. Cancer's role in my body is redundant.

Thank You
I came here so afraid of everything
So worn down and bruised
Deep within me, I knew I had to be here
to heal completely
I was guided to you!
Through your compassion
I have found myself
My broken heart has healed.
Now full of love and
open to all life's precious gifts
Thank- you for this oasis
and your amazing care.
Josh and I will live as
we have never lived before!
Dear Jesus, thank-you.

21st March 07: As we drive away from Issels, I feel renewed. I feel cherished and precious. This has been such a remarkable time in my life. I want to hold Issels close to me as I travel home alone. The cab driver drives me to the airport in San Diego. He kindly stays with me until I get a wheel chair. I have never done this before and it is a bit of a hurdle. But, pride aside, I need all the help I can find to make sure my trip home is as effortless as possible. I check-in, pointing out that my case of vaccines need to be taken on as hand luggage. This goes smoothly. One of the ground staff wheels me through security, which is a great help. I have to open the box of vaccines, which concerns me. After checking the contents and feeling satisfied, I arrive at my departure gate. My flight departs in two hours time. One hour later, one of the ground crew approaches the departure gate. I ask him if someone can carry the box of vaccines, as it is too heavy for me. Then the drama unfolds. After opening the box yet again, the attendant points out that there is too much dry ice, which is not allowed on to the plane. I have to return to check-in, which is too onerous. I am taken by wheelchair to check-in, where my box is opened yet again and all the dry ice put on the weighing scales! At this point, I am beside myself and terribly upset. This precious, expensive, cancer vaccine is defrosting before my eyes. After a further twenty minutes, most of the dry ice is removed. I then have three minutes to catch the plane, and still have to go through security yet again! This is a nightmare: I had anticipated it but not to this extent. I make the flight with seconds to spare. I am exhausted. I try hard to calm down. This drama is still not finished. As I wait for the plane to take off, one of the air hostesses asks me if I would like to get off the plane as one of my vaccines had been left at check-in (probably stuck to some removed dry ice). I cannot believe I am hearing this. I do not have the energy to go through this again, so I decline, prepared to leave it behind. Then the drama starts to take a different turn, thank goodness. The pilot steps in and states that he will hold the plane until the missing vaccine is brought to me on board. I am relieved and very grateful. Later on, the air hostess offers me some valuable advice for my connecting flight, suggesting that I ask the air cabin crew if they can let me have some of the dry ice in which the air meals are packed, after they have served the food to passengers. This advice proves invaluable, as the aircrew on my connecting flight help me repack my vaccines. I can rest now and regain my energy for meeting Josh at London Airport. I can't wait!

I leave the plane feeling excited yet also a little anxious. I still have to get through customs, collect my baggage without getting too tired. To my relief, a wheelchair is waiting for me. This takes the strain. I advise any cancer patient not to struggle alone but ask for help. Lack of energy alone is good enough reason to need a wheelchair. There are no medals for self – sacrifice.

I collect my luggage and leave Departures. I let go of the wheelchair, as I do not want to concern Josh unnecessarily. My heart is pounding as I come through into the arrivals area. I can see Josh in the distance, playing with Simon and not looking in my direction. I can't help but feel disappointed. I am so excited and just want to rush up to Josh and hug him to bits. Yet, I also know that this has been a long parting and it will take time for us to bond again. I call out 'Josh' and he looks up and smiles. We all say 'hello'. Josh is distracted and distant. This is difficult. I know we have both missed each other so much. This reminds me painfully of those days when I used to leave Josh at home while I travelled throughout the UK, working. Josh was only a baby then. When I came home, Josh would not look me in the eyes for several hours. Looking back to those years, this must have been so difficult for him. But now my time away has been for such different reasons. We both will experience the benefits in the months and years ahead.

As we get into Simon's car at the airport, Josh wants to sit in the back alone. I sit in the front. We start chatting on our way home, building bridges gently and steadily. When we get home, one and half hours later Josh and I hug each other. This is the best feeling in the world. This has been the bravest thing Josh and I have done since I got ill. By parting from each other for a whole month, we have had to really let go, otherwise neither of us would have pulled through and coped. In my case, I knew that if I brought worry about Josh with me to Issels, it would impede my body's vital healing. I also knew that Josh had to become part of Angie's family during my time away. When he referred to Angie's family as 'we' in his emails, I knew that this had happened. I can't really express my mixed emotions, wanting Josh to be okay but missing my boy so much and having to let him go at the same time.

Trecool by Josh

Angie thoughtfully bought a rabbit for Josh, which he named: 'Trecool', as mentioned in his emails. Josh looked after Trecool at Angie's while I was away. This is the only sketch that Josh did while we were apart. I see a little rabbit safely enclosed and protected in his hutch, not daring to venture outside. Perhaps this was how it was for Josh during this difficult time.

26th March 07: I am so glad to be home with my boy. At the same time I miss my wonderful friends in Issels and the caring ethos of that unique place. My friend Simon is staying with us for the week, which is so helpful. I don't want to speak to any friends for a few days. I feel that I am surrounded in a cloak of warmth, love and healing. I only want my son close to me in my sacred space. Simon being here allows Josh and I time to adjust to home life again.

22

Taking Control

30 March'07 I feel very anxious about being able to continue my
health routine now that I have come home. I am all too aware
that I do not have the help that I have had in Issels. With
Simon's help for this week, I am working out a plan for myself
which includes the following:

My Wholistic Healing Regime
- supplements every day with meals
- one enema every day/ 2 enemas during vaccines
- 3/4 glasses of fresh organic vegetable juice daily
- 3 organic meals
- Injections of Coley's vaccine every other week x 6
  months
- Injection of Dendritic cell vaccine every other week x 6
  months
- Injections of Issels vaccines every other week x 6
  months
- Herceptin intravenously every 3 weeks
- Zoladex injection every 4 weeks

I have just typed this out in colour and pasted it on one of
my kitchen cupboards to guide me through each day: I decide to
prepare all my supplements the night before, to take three times a
day. I will do my enema each morning or evening depending on
how I am feeling. On the weeks of the vaccines, I shall give
myself one or two enemas daily. I will attempt to prepare three
vegetable juices each day. This is probably the most time-
consuming exercise, as the vegetables need to be fresh and
organic, washed and cut into manageable pieces for juicing.
Finally the juicer needs to be thoroughly cleaned after use each
time, as juice loses its goodness if left for too long, I shall need to

prepare each juice from scratch. I intend to have one juice after breakfast, one after lunch and one after dinner. Josh will be able to help me and earn some extra pocket money too. I shall shop regularly every week and have Tesco deliver to my home once a month. The thought of all this is quite daunting but I am committed to this treatment. Last, but by no means least, are the vaccines.[13] The Coley's Mixed Bacterial Vaccine is a subcutaneous injection given into my lower stomach on the Monday of every second week. Initially Wendy former school matron from Josh's school, has kindly offered to give me this shot but I hope to be able to do it myself quite soon. Not bad for a needle phobic! The Dendritic Cell Vaccine is a muscular injection given into both of my upper legs on the Wednesday of the same week. I don't think that I shall be able to master this myself, so will have to rely on Wendy's kindness. The Issels Autologous Vaccine is a subcutaneous injection given into my inside leg on the Saturday of the same (second) week. Again Wendy will help me out initially but I hope soon to be able to do this myself. At least I have two weeks to prepare before starting this regime.

1st April 07: Starting the vaccines is an ordeal. As Wendy inserts the needle I start sobbing and become very upset, but Wendy remains calm and soothes me, enabling me to get through this ordeal. I know this will get easier as I get used to Wendy and begin to trust her. Her compassion and understanding towards me makes all the difference.

17th April 07: I am not looking forward to going back to the hospital for my next lot of Herceptin. Having experienced Issels, going back into the NHS system does not inspire me. I feel strangely detached and relaxed as I walk into the chemo suite. I feel enveloped in a protective layer of love and hope The Issels treatment combined with my medical treatment here in the NHS give me the wholistic treatment that I have been searching for all along. Two of the chemo nurses come to give me my Herceptin

---

[13] See Appendix G1 at end of this book for a description of the vaccines and their specific functions.

– one to hold my hand and one to insert the canula. They comment that I may be missing my friend, but I know I am fine. They are surprised by my much calmer reaction to the canula. What usually was quite a traumatic day for me is now very relaxed.

28th April 07: After only two lots of vaccines, I am now able, with Wendy's help, to give myself my Coley's and Issels' vaccines. Watching as I insert the needle into my own skin takes my breath away, yet at the same time seems to breathe life into me. The Dendritic vaccine is another matter, but I do not need to scale Everest as well today.

7th May 07: I feel very emotional today as my friend Julie and I approach the Finish line at the end of Cancer Research UK's sponsored five kilometre 'Race for Life', or rather walk in our case. This marks the end of my cancer. Back in 2004 I associated Finish with my death. I never for one minute back then ever conceived of even surviving cancer, let alone living so contentedly. Cancer has given Josh and I so much. We are truly blessed.

Later today I receive a surprising call from Amy Lewis, of ITV News, who has heard of our experience through another cancer patient considering Issels treatment. As a result, Amy wants to interview Josh and I about our story. Prior to our TV interview I spend time chatting to Josh about my trip. I want to help him get used to answering questions so that he will not be too nervous for the interview. When I ask him if he worried about me while I was away so long, his reply surprises me: 'Not really, mum, 'cos they were not carving you up' Then I ask him what he thinks they were doing: 'Putting good things into you'. Whilst I have been primarily concerned with cancer, Josh has been worried about my surgeries in hospital, when the doctors 'carved me up'. I feel that, even now, Josh is not entirely happy with my left 'flat' chest: 'Mum, that side of your chest was more puffy after your surgery. Now it seems to have got flatter.' How do I explain to my son that there may be less of my body, but there is so much more of me inside? Not an easy task!

4th June 07: Josh goes to school as usual today but comes home early, at eleven, in good time to meet the interviewer and cameraman from ITV. They are due to arrive at twelve noon. My friend Claire arrives at the same time as Josh. It is great to see her again. We became so close after having gone together to Issels in Mexico. I feel excited. This is almost surreal. We are about to be interviewed on television about our lives. Having come through these three healing years and out the other side, I do not feel 'in it' anymore. Josh and I both know we are in a great place within ourselves.

Amy and Ian, her cameraman, present a warm, professional face of ITV. Amy's warmth and sensitivity to our situation helps us relax. The interview gets underway with Amy interviewing both Josh and I. I don't recall much of this but I feel Josh beside me throughout. When I look at him, little tears are pouring down his face. Then I realise that I am talking about how I was feeling when I was initially diagnosed. Josh has not previously heard my thoughts at this first vulnerable time. Amy is upset as well. We all agree to pause for a moment. Feeling our way through situations like this is what brings us through. I turn to Josh quietly and bring him back to how we are now: 'You know darling that I am okay right now' He nods. Amy continues by interviewing Claire separately which gives us some time out. Josh, of course, has not heard Claire speak about our experience before. Having this break gives us both a little time to relax. This pause in the interview is important, allowing Josh to gather his thoughts and feelings. It is still hard for me to grasp the fact that this interview is how about Josh and I have lived with cancer.

Ian, the cameraman, then wisely suggests that Josh and I do some juicing in the kitchen. We both enjoy this. Josh loves earning a little more money. It is funny. I feel that I am doing a recipe on early morning telly. After this I notice that Josh is getting on very well with Ian, so we both think that it might be better if they work together. We women stay out of it. It works. Josh starts sketching, which he loves, and Amy asks him a few questions towards the end. I find watching and listening to my boy so moving. He has been so brave throughout our journey.

As he grows up and as his artistic talent develops he will have a wealth of passion and experience within his little soul to draw upon.

8th June 07: Josh and I are going to stay with friends for the weekend. I am delighted to say that I have forgotten that I have an appointment to see my oncologist. So I decide to bring Josh with me to the hospital and he can wait in the Maggie Cancer Centre while I see Dr. Lavery. Afterwards we can go on to our friends, as it is in the same direction. I smile to myself. I would never have even considered bringing Josh to the hospital before. It was the 'sharp end' in my mind. But now there are no sharp ends.

Nothing hangs on these appointments anymore, regardless of what Dr. Lavery tells me. This is wonderful. 'I am in heaven yet here on earth'. Dr. Lavery immediately notices the difference in me. I am on my own, relaxed and confident. She wants to know what has made the difference. Surprisingly she is interested in what I experienced at The Issels Clinic. I had underestimated her interest in wholistic cancer treatments. After three years of the NHS, a detached and objective attitude of doctors is what I have come to expect. I would love some oncologists from UK to be able to visit The Issels Clinic and experience the ethos of that Oasis. Sadly I suspect that hell might freeze over first.

22nd June 07: Josh comes home from school today and hands me his school report. I read it with tears in my eyes. Josh has done so well. The following section from his Head of Year reassures me that Josh has grown through this experience:

'This is a very encouraging report, which clearly reflects Josh's potential to achieve a great deal. I have seen a huge change in him since September, and he is growing into a far more confident, out-going individual. Given the difficulties that Josh has been faced with this year, he should be hugely congratulated for his efforts. I am well aware that he must have found it incredibly difficult to concentrate at times, and yet his will and determination have shone through. I am very proud to have him in my year group and I truly wish him every success for the future. Keep up that positive work-ethic, Josh.'

Head of Year

1st July 07: At church today, these words catch my attention and sum up our experience beautifully:

'Father of all, we give you thanks and praise,
That when we were still far off
You met us in your son and brought us home
Dying and living, he declared your love,
Gave us grace, and opened the gate of glory.
May we who share Christ's body live his risen life;
We who drink his cup bring life to others;
We whom the spirit lights give light to the world.
Keep us firm in the hope you have set us free,
And the whole earth live to praise your name;
Through Christ our Lord. Amen

12th July 07: Today is my 'physical' birthday but 27th February will always represent my spiritual birthday and Issels my spiritual home.

A few days later, two of my friends and Josh and I are preparing to watch our televised interview this evening. A strange mix of eager anticipation and anxiety bubble up inside me. The prospect of seeing ourselves on national TV, exposing our truth to millions of strangers feels unreal, yet important and valuable. As our interview begins, I take a deep breath in. I am shocked at how vulnerable we appear, yet how strong I feel inside. I finally let my breath out and cuddle my boy with tremendous pride, inner strength and love.

As I struggle to add the finishing touches to our story, I realise that cancer with all its amazing gifts, has been our life for the past three years. The sheer number of tiresome trips to the hospital has been unbelievable! In total to date: more than a hundred hospital appointments, 6 surgical procedures, thirteen radiotherapy sessions, seven CT scans, two X-rays, three Echo heart scans, endless blood tests, thirteen Zoladex injections, eighteen Herceptin treatments… and still counting.

This is only my medical treatment. My complementary appointments are much more empowering for me.[14] And they say: 'Don't let cancer take over your life!' I don't know what is more exhausting: the shock of diagnosis, the debilitating effects of clinical treatment, the 'charged' appointments with the oncologist or the actual organisation and time involved in incorporating all this into life itself: or, more to the point, incorporating our lives into cancer!. I am amazed that I managed to keep life going at all at home while working at the same time! When did I have time to be ill? But, of course, what I didn't realise was how much I needed that precious time. My chosen stay at the Issels Clinic was my salvation. Saying that I would not let cancer take over our lives was unrealistic. Josh and I as a family were catapulted into the torturous world of cancer upon diagnosis. Before I had time to find my feet, cancer had grabbed us physically and psychologically, its spider-like effect extending beyond my body, drawing in all those around me, as well. In fact, I would go so far as to say that I have got used to having cancer in our lives so that leaving it is a wrench, in a strange sort of way. Cancer helped me change and heal. Now it is time to take the next step. Rising above cancer continually requires great inner strength, wicked determination, tenacity, positive attitude and one hell of a sense of humour. I feel torn between stalling, not wanting to let go of our story and wanting to move on. I guess that I am a little sad.

---

[14] See full list of appointments at Appendix I at the end of the book

23

Coming Out

2008

11th-27th April 08: Josh and I are returning to The Issels
Treatment Centre just over a year later. What a different
experience this for us turned out to be – even more illuminating
and empowering, but for us both on this occasion. The
following verses sum up my innermost thoughts as I leave for
Issels this time.

Coming Out

I want to come out
hold me tight till I can stand
alone in the light
and shine!
flickering in shadow
unsteady and slight
uncertain, unsure
to love or fight?
will it hurt
will I be alright
will I die?
can I breathe in the light?

I feel proud and confident walking into Issels with Josh.
We have survived and healed, after our month apart a year ago.
I never thought for a moment back then that we would be
returning together. Josh relaxes quite quickly after being warmly
welcomed by everyone. 'Mum, everyone seems to know you
here' he says after the first day. I feel that I have come home
and I am surprised at how quickly and easily I have slotted back
into the Issels regime of infusions, juices, meals and, most

importantly, prayer sessions. I want it all. I have felt thirsty for the whole atmosphere of Issels.

It's wonderful eating with other patients and their partners in the dining room. Josh seems to be settling in really well and actually enjoying this healing and loving atmosphere. On the evening of the fourth day of our hospital stay, I attend evening prayers as Josh goes out with some other patients to El Yoghurt – a local organic restaurant. I sit in prayers, touched deeply by other patients' heart-rending experiences, involving incredible courage and faith. This powerful, safe atmosphere inspires me to share 'newfound' vulnerabilities from the depth of my being. Feeling such a deep connection with everyone, the almost palpable triumph of faith over adversity is incredibly humbling.

As I step forward for healing, I know that I want to put my cancer firmly behind me now and move on with my new path in life as we return home. As others lay their hands on me, holding me up in prayer, I clearly see: Josh and I stumbling along a long, bumpy path holding hands. In front of us and a little to the left, a huge, blazing fire is roaring. We let go of each other as I walk through the raging fire, while Josh walks along on the far side always level with me. As I emerge from the fire, purged and healed, Josh and I meet and walk on contentedly together.

Like the passage from the Bible, Daniel 3 verses 19-25 relating to Shadrach, Medshach and Abednego::

'And these three men Shadrach, Meshach and Abednego, fell down bound into the midst of the burning fiery furnace. Then Nebuchadnezzar the king was astonished, and rose up in haste, and spake and said unto his counsellors. 'Did not we cast three men bound into the midst of the fire?' They answered and said unto the King. 'True, O King'.

He answered and said. 'Lo, I see four men loose, walking in the midst of the fire, and they have no hurt, and the form of the fourth is like the Son of God.' Similiarly, and very unexpectedly, I did not walk through my fire alone.

When Mrs Issels invites me to do a videoed testimonial for uploading on to the Issels website,[15] I am delighted to be able to show our support. Josh and I meet Raul – the cameraman in the prayer room – the ideal location. Josh sits out of my sight, while I sit in the middle of the room, water running behind me, by the illuminated statue of the blind man (whom Jesus healed).

'And it came to pass, that as he was come nigh unto Jericho, a certain blind man sat by the wayside begging. And hearing the multitude pass by, he asked what it meant. And they told him, that Jesus of Nazareth passeth by. And he cried, saying, Jesus, thou Son of David have mercy on me. And they which went before rebuked him, that he should hold his peace: but he cried so much the more. Thou Son of David have mercy on me. And Jesus stood, and commanded him to be brought unto him: and when he was come near, he asked him. Saying, what wilt thou that I should do onto thee? And he said, Lord that I may receive my sight. And Jesus said onto him, Receive thy sight, thy faith hath saved thee. And immediately he received his sight, and followed him, glorifying god and all the people, when they saw it, gave praise onto God.' Luke 18 verses 35-43

Raul asks me to talk for about three or so minutes about my experience here at Issels. I take a deep breath and steady myself. After these surprisingly, emotional minutes, Josh and I have a cuddle. Then after repeating it all again for the camera, I relax. However, this does not seem quite right without Josh also being involved. Then, spontaneously, I ask Josh if he would like to be part of this video, as he is part of my Issels experience this time. He nods and I reassure him that he will not have to say anything unless he wants to. As I rearrange my chair, with Josh sitting just behind my right shoulder, I marvel silently at this amazing scene which I could never have foreseen, in my wildest dreams, four years ago when I was diagnosed

I relate our experience again, but more fully this time, evolving and deepening as I continue. Gentle words of love and

---

15 www.issels.com

gratitude to the most important person in my life, Josh, make their way through my tears of joy.

When I think about it, everything about our trip to Mexico has been concerned with looking after our insides (infusions, vegetable juices, organic food or sharing vulnerable moments with other patients during prayers, vaccines, even enemas) and taking time with other patients and our missionary friends, Bruce and Vicky. A couple of patients remark how different I look during this holiday week after having been a patient a week prior. I think that as a patient at Issels I bare my soul, voicing all my concerns, worries, doubts regarding my health, physically, emotionally and spiritually and, after detoxifying, non-toxic treatment on all levels, I emerge stronger and recharged.

What a change from my previous 'shallow' existence when my every waking moment was focussed on maintaining a successful outward appearance and Super Woman status. This included acquiring countless material possessions for my home, garden, car; wearing the latest fashion, jewellery, shoes; membership of prestigious health club, expensive holidays: all pursued through an 'endlessly achieving' lifestyle mixed with unfulfilling relationships. It feels as though I have turned myself inside out, and I love it. Material things matter less and less: relationships with God, my son Josh and my close friends matter more and more. I feel a contentment deep inside that is in no way dependent on external factors. I love communicating from this very deep, precious part of me and want to continue doing so. This is how I can help others. I have found a truly deep connection with other patients here, borne of a humility, respect and complete awe for their remarkable courage and love. Words cannot really express my sense of connection. I feel humbled and loved. This all feels so new.

Towards the end of our second week with our missionary friends Josh and I both pop back to the hospital. I have some blood taken to make up the Issels vaccine, for me to collect in six months time. Naively, I think that this will take a few moments. As we enter our old room, Josh promptly jumps on to the guest bed with his PSP (play station portable) and I perch myself on the patient bed stretching out my right arm. After one failed attempt, Ricardo, the Haematologist explains that as I am so nervous, my muscle actually jumps and moves my vein. I have not heard the consequences of my anxiety described in these words before. He comments that there is very little I can do about that. So we have another failed attempt, as I grip the infusion tree beside me and hum as well. Poor Josh; he cannot abide my singing attempts. Ricardo even suggests that he might have to try my left arm on this one occasion. I am very reluctant, as I have had some lymph nodes removed from my right arm back in 2004. However, I am determined to stay here until he gets hold of my blood. So after another little rest, we try again – all three of us this time! This time I close my eyes and see Jesus' face while Josh sits by me: but no luck. I have one more trick up my sleeve. I wince as I start clenching my fist, willing my vein to relax. I start singing:

'O lord you are beautiful
Your face is all I seek
For when your eyes are on this child
Your grace abounds in me'

And I keep repeating this verse, even attempting translation into Spanish, with Ricardo filling in the difficult words for me, while drawing my blood. Josh's gaze is transfixed on my arm and excitedly tells me that my blood is coming out quickly. Ricardo gives me the excellent news that I am completely relaxed and my blood is 'gushing out'. 'So keep singing.' When I ask if he has enough blood he replies that he only has nine vials but needs four more. I don't care how many he needs. His parting shot is: 'Next time, Jacinta, try to sing that hymn at the beginning'.

During the remaining few days Josh and I spend some time in the hospital socially. I find a new confidence and sense of detachment this time. Being here as a family is rewarding beyond words. This second visit to Issels marks our moving on together in celebration and hope. As I spend time with patients, some very poorly, I visualise a powerful, strong, loving hand gently drawing each patient up and out of their cancers. A former Issels patient and close friend Carolyn, from the UK, described her Issels experience: 'We are all a bit lost over here but Issels is like a community'. Issels within the Oasis of Hope Hospital is not solely a successful, wholistic immunotherapy treatment centre, it is a community where we eat together, pray together, have treatment whilst helping and loving each other. It is an OASIS where we meet in an atmosphere of trust and hope and emerge from our cancers as the unique, special individuals we are. As we leave I know in my heart that I will be back as a patient but, more importantly, I also hope to be able to return as a volunteer at some point.

Josh and I with our missionary friends Bruce and Vicky

Back home, Josh settles into school again with a new confidence and maturity. I go along to see my oncologist with my friend Auriel, although this time it feels more like a social visit. I just feel so well, contented and at peace, full of gratitude and eager to help others, here and in Mexico. When I mention that I want to do talks on 'Post- mastectomy Sex', for instance, I don't think Dr. Lavery can believe her ears. However, once we begin to discuss my offer to help others in this way, there appears to be a real need and value in patients' open and honest expression and discussion of their own personal experiences and triumphs through cancer. I relate our great experience in Mexico this time. Dr. Lavery responds by asking rhetorically, in her usual measured, mellow tone, if that perhaps means that I am happy to continue with Zoladex and Herceptin?

'Well Dr. Lavery, I bet on a horse in The Grand National this year 'Comply or Die' and, guess what, my horse won. I chose this particular horse within seconds for its name only. Hence, my decision to continue with my treatment. She looked up to heaven, whispering: 'Thank you, God'. Actually doctors at The Issels Treatment Centre, Dr. Lavery and God within me, have all contributed to my decision. My bet simply confirmed my subconscious thinking. As Dr. Lavery rightly commented: 'You know, Jacinta, that we do not know whether you still need this treatment or not, at this stage, but consider it as the price you pay.' This is truly the only price I have paid. Everything else has been a precious gift!

24

Complete

4th August 09: Sitting in church, desperately trying to join in, singing hymns and fighting tears away, my body trembling and eating the air as I splutter out each note. So many mixed feelings devour my shaky frame, bursting to be heard. A friend sits next to me and, in a barely audible whisper, guides me outside. Tears well up as I give way to the fear, doubt and anxiety welling up inside me: 'I don't know whether to go to Derry or not, I am afraid of getting hurt. I don't feel very strong. I want Josh to have a good time and not to see me hurting. Should I contact my family. I am not sure. Yet I want to go. My friend Lyn listens and my soul quietens.

As we make our way early to the airport the following morning, uncertainty retains a somewhat lighter grip. Going through Departures, a sea of people stretches out before us in an endless queue for security. Shuffling slowly along, my doubt returns, dominating my thoughts. Stripping ourselves of our metal, we clear security and we head for the departure gate. Searching the electronic screens quickly to find the gate number for our flight, my heart stops in disbelief: 'Gate closed' stares back at us. What gate, when, where? Desperately finding a phone, I hear that our flight has actually departed. In shock, and £76 later, we check in again for the next flight, only to find that we almost miss this one as well. Suddenly, to my son's amazement, I burst into a determined run to the gate. 'Mum, you are running!'. With an unexpected determination, I shout: 'We are going to Ireland Josh'. My desire to go home has finally broken through my fear and uncertainty, filling me with newfound energy and excitement.

Meeting up with Geraldine and her husband Paul at Belfast airport is wonderful and I can't wait to get to Derry. Geraldine is my best friend from school days and through more than thirty years without much contact and very separate lives, we have remained close friends. Her spontaneous reaction to my cancer diagnosis five years ago – offering to board a plane straight away to be with me and Josh, took my breath away.

Approaching Derry, gently dipping into darkness, I ask Paul if he will drive though the city centre before taking us to our hotel. Feeling like a child again, I gasp as I catch a glimpse of Shipquay Street, the main street where we first lived above the bank where daddy worked. Looking down Shipquay Street, bathed in moonlight as it slopes away to the River Foyle, warms my heart. I want so much of this. As we settle into our hotel this evening, I can't believe that I am back home. I can't wait to show Josh my home town and give him a real sense of his Irish background.

My friend collects us the next morning and asks us where we would like to go first. We want to go to mammy and daddy's grave, as it's nearby. It's so long since I have been here that I am unsure of what this means to me now. Driving in through the cemetery gates, I see the grave straight ahead and point it out to Josh. As we stand in front of it, all I can see are the words: 'In loving memory…' I feel at home and proud to tell Josh about his grandparents. My little stone still rests there: 'Now you shall truly dance'. Those words mattered so much to me sixteen years ago, but now they seem no longer needed and rest easily alongside the main headstone. Together we carefully tend to the grave, cleaning the headstone and planting a flowering plant. Surprisingly Josh then asks me: 'Where is the lady who helped you when your mummy died?' and so we walk past several more graves in the same row to find the grave of my friend Nuala. Suddenly the heavens open, shrouding the entire cemetery in a veil of mist. Just about managing to force our huge umbrella open against the pounding rain, we happily curl up on a nearby bench. Threads of heavenly, colourful light magically filter through the broken clouds, bathing misty memories of the past in a love and peace that is tinged with surrealism.

The following morning, after a restful sleep, I bounce out of bed wide awake, eager for what this new day has to bring. For Josh it's a different matter: he is still sound asleep and is reluctant to share my early morning enthusiasm. Later we drive into Derry town centre with Geraldine and stop outside the Bank House – my original home, although the building has changed in many ways. Standing outside where the front door to our home used to be, I look for the little barred window at ground level where I used to spend hours as a child gazing out on to the street above. But it has gone. I feel disappointed. Geraldine then mentions that she remembers it, which lifts me a little. I wanted to show it to Josh. My hand touches the wall in a vain attempt to check it is real and that this is really happening. This feels good. Going round to the front and down a few steps, we find a hospice shop where the cellar would have been. Knocking on the door, I dive straight in, explaining that I lived here, as if this gives us right of passage. The shop is due to open in the following few days. Josh and I walk around trying to pinpoint where the cellar was. I think it was further down, only to be reassured by the owner that there is nothing below where we are. So perhaps it has been filled in with cement and buried deep below the ground. Sharing this with my son, with such good feelings, is amazing. As we leave, I am heartened to know that the proceeds of this new hospice shop will all go to the care of children with cancer. This all feels as it should be.

Today we are off to Buncrana, a little coastal town fourteen miles from Derry. Daddy was also Branch Manager of a smaller bank here. I don't think I have been back here since I was a little girl. I recall going down on the bus with him and playing around in the back office. 'There's the bank, it's still there!' I am amazed. Then Josh asks me if we are near the beach where we all used sometimes to go as a family on Sundays. Geraldine and Paul park near the beach. My heart lightens, and skips with real excitement. Pushing Josh's beanie on to my head, in the rain and strong winds, we both run down to the beach. The years peel away with each step we take. Josh excitedly asks me: 'Where is the exact spot you all sat when you used to come here?' 'Just there Josh, right on that rock', I reply with a sense of achievement and pride. I run up the rocks and standing at the top, arms outstretched to the heavens, I beam from ear to ear, complete in every way.

As I scramble down again, Josh climbs up and, smiling, waves down to me. A wave of pride wells up inside me. As Geraldine later comments: 'Its amazing how a simple scene – a small stretch of beach with worn rock formations and blustering winds – can be so fulfilling in so many different ways.

After loading our bags into Geraldine's car we stop at a florists and I carefully choose a large bunch of twelve white roses. Visiting the cemetery one last time, Josh and I place six roses in the glass vase in pride of place next to mammy and daddy's headstone. Moving on to Nuala's grave, we lay four roses carefully on the grass. As we walk back to the car Geraldine joins us and offers to water the graves regularly after we have gone. Saving the best to last, a rose for each of our caring angels, Geraldine and Paul. As we leave this silent resting place and head home, my heart surrenders. I love my parents after all.

25

Looking Back

I don't know what was worse – my mother's drink-induced psychotic episodes or my father's weakness and betrayal of my trust. What I do know is that it has taken me much longer to confront my internalised anger and shame as a result of my father's abusive behaviour, and without cancer this would have been impossible. What I am very sure of is that the buck stops here – my son does not carry this legacy on.

When I go back to my earliest memory of childhood, I see myself as a little toddler lying in my cot: Mammy is standing over me, dressed up, her steely bazookas out in front, her cold eyes piercing my little frame: 'You may be the apple of your father's eyes but you will never take him away from me'. I shudder, remembering such terrible beginnings.

I was so many people as a child: the lovely little girl who always wanted some of daddy's attention; the burdened, ashamed, guilty little girl who made daddy abuse her; the overly responsible little girl who always worried about daddy when hearing and seeing mammy abusing him; the surrogate little parent who tried to look out for her younger brother and sister; the isolated little girl who sat for hours patiently in the cellar, waiting for daddy to let her out; the good, little girl who tried so very hard to be everything mammy wanted her to be; and the abandoned little girl who jumped through hoops to spend some time with daddy.

Looking back now, I cannot help but wonder if my mother's constant focus on the pain of childbirth and her prediction that I could not have a normal child was her perception of the consequence of my father's incest. Enforcing my isolation from my father, my brother and sister could perhaps have been her inept attempt to protect my brother and sister from my father and me.

Broken trust has been the most damaging and lasting stigma from my childhood. In spite of endless years of therapy, I have been unable to release this broken part of me. This heavy burden has silently and secretly eaten not just into my body but into my whole life.

Cancer has shown me how to really appreciate life and to live it freely in love and peace. I do not believe that I could have unearthed these gifts without my earlier background and life experience. Had life been more fulfilling and my self-esteem remained intact then I imagine that my reactions to cancer would have been quite different and, cancer, for different reasons, harder to bear. This realisation and understanding has helped me in my darkest hours to find an inner strength, a determination and innate power to rise high above the ashes of my childhood and uneasy life. In the face of the clinical detachment of our health service but with the encouragement and support of my close friends, I dug deep within myself to find my little voice boldly expressing my thoughts and feelings throughout my treatment, ensuring that I made my own decisions and sought the wholistic treatment that I believed I needed. The image that comes to mind is of the lower half of my body submerged in thick, dark, sticky glue: with my face looking upwards towards the heavens and every vein and muscle in my neck pulsating, I pull myself upwards with every ounce of my being. Cancer has shown me the way out of my own prison and stunted existence.

I am finally finding myself after many lonely, anxious, often painful years of searching in the wrong places, mistakenly thinking that meeting the right man and getting married would make all the difference. Little did I know that it was much simpler than that, yet so much more difficult to access – an inner strength, power and 'godness' inside me all this time. I am steadily regaining the trust that I lost as a child. I am amazed at how scary this has sometimes been, but at the same time absolutely liberating!

My recent dream encapsulates my sense of forgiveness and peace: 'I am in town shopping when I spot mammy standing small and alone outside Marks and Spencers in the High Street.

She smiles, looking relieved as she sees me approaching. I put my arm around her shoulders and suggest we go uptown together. Further on, I see Daddy leaning on his walking stick, tilting his hat and smiling peacefully as he sees us together. 'Mammy, let's join daddy and go uptown together'. I put one arm around his stooped shoulders and my other around mammy's. Together we all go shopping'.

We always have choices when faced with challenges, no matter how difficult those challenges may be. These choices may not be easy ones but they are choices nonetheless. The vital key is recognising we always have the power to choose. We can carry on trying to keep our lives going as they were, thinking that we will not let cancer change us: or we can begin to look at our lives and slowly make healthy changes, letting go of the stresses and emotional baggage that we are carrying, and take the opportunity to give ourselves the break we really need, to really look after ourselves mentally, physically and emotionally.

I am so proud to have been able, with the power of God, with the love and courage of my son with my family of friends and cancer itself, to go back to that dreadful cellar and bring my beautiful little girl up to the light, to truly shine, as God intended from the very beginning. This is my gift to you.

Appendices

Appendix A

SPACE – Anne Smith   www.Aylesburyspace.co.uk
Providing support and care in difficult times.
Everyone goes through difficult times once in a while. You may feel alone and isolated. These times can be difficult and even traumatic, but organisations like SPACE can offer you support.
We support people who are going through relationships difficulties, depression, bereavement, unemployment, mental health problems, loneliness, or any combination of these issues.
You are not alone! We can support you by providing:
A safe place to unwind and think
Someone who will listen to you without judgement and in confidence
Information about other organisations
A chance to meet with others
What can I expect from SPACE?
A free and confidential listening service
Weekly group drop-ins on Tuesdays and Fridays, 10.30am to 12 noon
A Sunday drop-in from 2pm to 4pm
What happens at a drop-in?
There are trained and friendly listeners who can give you time in a quiet area, away from the group if this is what you want
All of what you say is kept in confidence
There is time to join with others, have a tea or coffee, chat and enjoy company
There is no fixed charge, but we ask for a small donation if you are able

Where are we?

SPACE, St, Mary's Church, St. Mary's Square, Aylesbury,
Busks, HP20 2JJ
We are based in St Mary's Church, St Mary's Square at the
top of Church Street close to the County Museum
Email: Aylesbury.space@btinternet.com
Telephone: 01296 432769
SPACE is open to all regardless of faith, age, sex, ethnic
origin, sexual orientation or disability
SPACE is a non-profit making organisation.
**Donations are gratefully received. Please contact Anne
on 01296 432769**

Appendix B

The Global Retreat Centre www.globalretreatcentre.org

Since 1993, the Global Retreat Centre has welcomed thousands of people from across the world. The centre offers residential and one-day retreats, as well as lectures, seminars and courses on meditation, personal growth and spiritual development. It is administered by the Brahma Kumaris World Spiritual University UK and, as a service to the community, charges no fees for any of its activities. It is funded by voluntary contributions.

Brahma Kumaris. The main principles in the Brahma Kumaris way of life are:

Study – The daily study of spiritual knowledge provides nourishment to create a healthy and stable mind.

Meditate – The practice of soul-consciousness creates inner strength to overcome negative self-belief. Connecting to God in a personal relationship removes blind faith and instils a deep sense of trust. The relationship charges the battery of the soul and fills it with love, peace and power.

Practise – To live a life dedicated to improving one's character by imbibing universal truths and higher motivations in thoughts, words and actions.

Serve – To share with others on the basis of one's own life experiences.

Retreats. All the retreats are led by experienced facilitators. They give their time freely, to help others see the inner changes which are necessary to cultivate a deeper contentment and a greater joy, in an often chaotic world. Each retreat is an opportunity to explore the deepest insights into the true nature of our being, review the purpose of our life and learn practical methods to sustain calm and clarity in everyday living. Both the one-day and residential meditation retreats provide experienced guidance in meditation, whilst the retreats for specific professional groups are designed to explore the application of spiritual values in the workplace.

Retreats at the Global Retreat Centre have two key components.

1. Examination of some of the deeper truths about human nature. We work with the understanding that there is an energy of goodness within us, and that this increases or decreases according to our habits of thought and feeling. Knowing more about ourselves, and how we function, gives us the power to think and act more positively.

2. Periods of silence in which to reflect on our higher feelings, values, and purpose in life. Peace of mind, intrinsic to all of us but easily lost when we become trapped in mundane concerns, is restored. This experience helps connect us to an unchanging and infinite source of love and truth.

The aim is to enable participants to recharge their own sense of well-being, and learn how to maintain this strength in everyday life. Lectures, workshops, pure vegetarian food, walks in the beautiful grounds, and a peaceful atmosphere all contribute to the process.

'From the beginning, the organisation's work has been based on the principle that spiritual knowledge is a basic right of every human being. It was the founder's (Brahma Baba's) aim to provide opportunities for everyone to develop their own spiritual potential, without charge, regardless of age, background or financial circumstances. This ethic is endorsed and reflected by all participating BK teachers and students. A calendar of events can be viewed on the following web link: http://www.globalretreatcentre.org/events

Appendix C

Health Creation   www.healthcreation.co.uk

Dr Rosy Daniel is founder and medical director of Health Creation, providing consultations for those with Cancer who are seeking advice on how to integrate alternative, complementary and self-help approaches to Cancer alongside orthodox medical treatment. She also provides support and guidance for those who cannot or choose not to have orthodox treatment.

Dr Daniel was former medical director of Bristol Cancer Help Centre (1993 to 1999), and worked from 1999 to 2005 at the Harley Consultant Oncology Centre. She addresses conferences and seminars nationally and internationally, and is a regular broadcaster. She is author of five books and the interactive cancer lifeline kit which can be accessed through the Health Creation website along with supportive health coaching from her Health Creation mentors. She has created this 'Health Creation Cancer Lifeline Support' service to provide the crucial long-term support to make the necessary lifestyle changes she recommends to her patients. She is also very concerned for the well-being of those caring for people with Cancer and to support them, has created the 'Health Creation Cancer Support' service.

Rosy has also developed a new coaching package known as 'Health Creation Proactive' for those seeking to prevent illness and generate high energy health and whole-hearted living. In this way she hopes to help reach individuals who wish to be supported to make healthy changes in their lifestyles, making a real difference to the incidence of Cancer and heart disease in the future.

Rosy Daniel's initial Recommendations:
1. Carctol – a herbal medicine which has been found to improve mental and physical well-being and help combat the adverse effects of radiotherapy.
   A digestive enzyme with each dose of Carctol
2. A wholefood, vegetarian, low acid, dairy free diet

3. Up to 3 litres of filtered water per day
4. Vegetable juices – ideally one full glass three times per day using carrots, beetroot, melon, broccoli, fennel, peppers, celery.
5. Vitamins and minerals, immune stimulants and digestive enzymes now available in one preparation called the "Lifeline Formula'

    Coriolus – 4 tablets 3 times per day for 3 months after medical treatment

    Max Immune based on 1-3, 1-6 Beta Glucan for immune stimulation
6. Help with State of Mind – use 'Cope Positively' CD for relaxation and then 'Images for healing Cancer' CD for helping to focus on your recovery and future. For counselling if needed, contact the centre for Transpersonal Psychology www.transpersonalcentre.co.uk
7. Energy support from a healer one – twice weekly
8. For long-term health, use The Health Creation Programme and health creation mentors for regular ongoing support, coaching and encouragement to achieve your health and life goals.
9. Litmus paper to check your pH levels

Appendix C1

Overview of alternative Cancer approaches to explore fall broadly into the following seven levels:

LEVEL 1 – Nutritional Metabolic – main UK expert Dr Etienne Callebout 0207255-2232

Strengthen your nutrition, tissue healing, digestion and immune system by Eating a wholefood, low acid, dairy free vegetarian diet high in essential fatty acids. Telephone consultations are available from Jane Sen on 01249-783243 via or the Health Creation website for her videos.

Making home-made vegetable juices.

Taking vitamins and minerals, Immune stimulants and digestive enzymes From Cytoplan on 01684-310099

a) Lifeline Formula – either as tablets – and take 5 tablets twice a day with food, or as powder and take 1 tsp of powder twice a day in soya milk.

b) Immune Boost – 1 capsule twice per day (Beta Glucan)

c) Fruits, Roots and Shoots – 1 capsule per day (Phytonutrients)

d) Omega 3 – 1 capsule per day

e) Carctol with a digestive enzyme tablet Cytozyme.

LEVEL 2 – Herbal – Dr Rosy Daniel

a) Detoxify and alkalinise the body by taking Carctol herbs

Avoid all acidic or sour food and drink (see acid-free diet info sheet)

Health Creation can supply a booklet of acid free recipes called 'Where's the Meat' by Gillian Gill

Drink up to 3 litres of clean water per day (either filtered bottled spring or boiled and cooled tap water)

Avoid constipation (take Senokot or Psylium Husks, if necessary)

Use litmus paper to check your pH (should be alkaline i.e. towards pH 8) Litmus paper is available from Health Creation on 0845-009-3366.

b) Take Salvestrol Gold and Salvestrol Professional – one capsule of each 2 times daily – available from The Nutri Centre. Information re Salvestrol can be found on their American website www.salvestrolscience.com

LEVEL 3 – Immunotherapy in Europe
a) Dr Nesselhut in Germany for Dendritic Cell Therapy on 0049 552 799710
b) Iscador treatment for immune stimulation on the NHS via referral from your GP to the Homeopathic Hospital in London, Glasgow, Bristol or Liverpool. You can also get it by finding a private anthroposophical doctor in your area by contacting Weleda UK, (who make Iscador), on 0115-9448200.

LEVEL 4 – Intravenous Metabolic
a) IV metabolic therapy is available from Dr Nicola Hembry in Bristol on 0117-9692814 or Dr Michael Wetzler in London on 07958-405877. Nicola also does chemo sensitivity testing to test for exact levels of cancer cell activity.

LEVEL 5 – Physical Therapies
a) Hyperthermia is available in Germany with Prof Douwes – 0049-8061-4980 and their sensitivity to chemotherapy and natural medicines.
b) Light therapy – Photo Dynamic Therapy is available from Dr Julian Kenyon at the Dove Clinic in Winchester on 01962-718000

LEVEL 6 – Mind-body Therapies For the mind and spirit:
a) Relax the body and focus the mind on recovery through the use first of the 'Cope Positively with Cancer Treatment' CD for relaxation and support through treatment and then the Images for Healing Cancer' CD for helping to focus on your recovery and future. The third CD is 'Heal Yourself' which has yoga and meditation exercises. (all from Health Creation)

b) For counselling if needed contact the centre for Transpersonal Counselling on 0208-203-6671 for a local referral or see www.transpersonalcentre.co.uk or Journey therapy with the Brandon Bays team – www.thejourney.com

c) Become energised and uplifted by spiritual healing once or twice weekly ideally. Ring the NFSH on 0845-123-2767 for extra help as needed. Acupuncture, Shiatsu or Reiki healing is also helpful.

LEVEL 7 – Health Creation Health Coaching

I have trained health creation mentors to support, guide and encourage my patients in their long term recovery. This service happens on the phone, or via the internet using SKYPE, which makes the calls free.

What you get out of the integrated approach to health will depend on how much you are able to make healthy changes in your behaviour and lifestyle. The Mentors are there to make sure that you make and sustain these healthy changes long-term, and that you keep going especially when life's other demands pick up again or at moments of peak vulnerability. To get the Health Creation Programme and a Mentor, talk to Mike on our Helpline (0845-009-3366).

Appendix D

Causal Natural Medicine Dr. Simi Khanna

Initially completed conventional medical training and worked for eight years as a hospital doctor. Her journey through grave illness and adversity led her through a multitude of experiences, discoveries and new ways of approaching health and life. She underwent further extensive training in these models and techniques leading to her practice of Causal Natural Medicine.

Her further training and qualifications are in: homeopathy, oxygen-ozone therapy, clinical nutrition, bioresonance and other forms of bioenergetic medicine. She trained in oxygen ozone therapy and pioneered its use in the U.K. She was one of the first medical practitioners to be awarded a Diploma in Bioresonance therapy and hold a diploma in Homeopathy. Her practice is the first to use 'pulsed ionic magnetic induction (PapIMI) therapy in U.K.

She works to prescribe an individualised health plan after appropriate consultation and screening for causal factors. This involves a synergistic combination of some of the most advanced and effective natural therapeutics.

The aim of using these therapies is a desire to assist the person effectively in their recovery and revitalisation. Dr. Simi has been helping patients recover since 1990. Unfortunately, due to personal reasons, she no longer practices in UK at this time.

Causal Natural Medicine

In recent decades, the inhabitants of the industrialised world have been subjected to mammoth changes in diet, chemicals and environment.

The working of the body and its genetics have been unable to adapt to this massive assault. As a result, there has been an unprecedented increase in chronic, degenerative and infectious illness.

Despite the ever-increasing pharmaceuticals, sophisticated medical tests and treatments, there are a growing number of people whose health and quality of life continue to deteriorate.

The major missing element in these treatments is the lack of adequate examination of the causal factors of disease. Furthermore, the treatments or solutions offered whether they be pharmaceutical, surgical or alternative do not address causal factors but focus on altering the body chemistry to reduce symptoms, offering; 'a pill for every ill' and 'a treatment for every ailment'.

This is an outdated approach, as mounting scientific evidence has established that the body chemistry is governed by the energy fields surrounding/within the body systems. As long as the integrity of these energy fields remain intact, so does our health. However, if these fields are altered or disturbed, disease process sets in.

What are the causal factors that disturb these energetic fields?

They are numerous and go far beyond just a bad diet. As the assaults from these continue, they result in toxic deposits and alterations in and around the body cells, leading to distortion of their energy and then the body chemistry. Unwellness and illness follow.

'Health is not just an absence of illness, but the positive balance of all aspects of a person – body, mind, emotions and spirit.'

What is the solution?

It follows therefore that for an effective solution, the causal factors that have disturbed these fields be located in the first instance. (It is futile to attempt to fit varied keys to a lock, without examining the lock first). The appropriate treatments which are provided, primarily strengthen/regulate the energy fields and then the chemistry of the body with means that do not suppress symptoms but enhance the body's innate powers to eliminate toxins, thereby resulting in recovery and wellness.

Noxious Causal Factors that Undermine Our Health

Emotional/Mental Factors	Biological Factors	Chemical Factors	Physical Factors
Undue Stress	Chronic Infections	Residual Pharmaceutical Toxins from Antibiotics, Hormones, Painkillers, Tranquilisers	Lack of Exercise, fresh air, sunlight
Conflicts	Residual Infective Agents		
Recurrent Upsets	Suppressed Discharges and Ailments		Structural/skeletal Misalignments
Relationship Problems	Non-optimum Dietary and Nutritional Factors	Contaminants in Air inside and outside buildings	Electromagnetic Stress e.g. from TV, computer, mobile phone, waterbed, electric blanket and other electrical equipment
Mental Circuits	Dental Materials – amalgam fillings, root canals, scars, cavitations	VOC Emissions from floor coverings, insulation, wallpaper, paints	
Communication Problems	Vaccination Side Effects		
Trauma Shocks	PH Imbalance (acid/alkaline)	Contaminated water/foodstuffs, preservatives, colourings, artificial sweetners, pesticide pesticides	Geomagnetic Stress
Negative, suppressed emotions	Disturbed Intestinal Flora		Heavy Metals e.g. mercury, lead, aluminium, cadmium, copper
	Immune System Insufficiencies and Hormone Imbalances	Recreational Drugs, Alcohol, Tobacco	
Others	Hypersensitivities/Allergic responses to Food, Chemicals, Heavy Metals, Electromagnetics		Constitutional, Metabolic and Genetic Weaknesses
	Inadequate Functioning and Congestion of Elimination and Detox Channels of the Body e.g. Bowel, Kidney, Liver, Lymph		
	Defects of Cellular Metabolism leading to inadequate oxygenation		
	Oxygen Depletion		

Who can benefit from causal natural medicine?

Any person suffering from short-term complaints or long-term illness who follows this model of health may be helped at this practice. People who have had good results using this approach, had the following conditions:

Acne, allergies/hypersensitivities, arthritis, angina pectoris, asthma, burnt out State, back pain/spinal pain, cardiovascular diseases, candidiasis, chronic fatigue, colitis, cystitis, crohn's disease, constipation, dental infections, diabetes, eczema, endometriosis, electromagnetic sensitivity, fibromyalgia, gout, heavy metal toxicity, headaches, high cholesterol, herpes infections, hypertension, hormonal problems, hypoglycaemia, inflammatory bowel disease, immune deficient states, infections (varied), irritable bowel syndrome, injuries, kidney and gall stones, leaky gut syndrome, mercury, amalgam toxicity, memory, concentration problems, neurological syndromes, prostate diseases, pain of various origins, recurrent infections, skin disorders, stomach/duodenal ulcers, sports injuries, tumours, thrush, thyroid problems

However, it is not the 'label' of the illness that is treated, but rather the person themselves, therefore the name or 'label' given to an illness is not that relevant.

Advanced Natural Therapeutics	
PapIM	Oxygen Ozone Therapy
Hyper Photon Soft Laser	UBVI
	Active Oxygen
BICOM Bioresonance	Therapeutic Infusions
QXCI	Homeopathy
Cyclotherm	

These therapies:

- Strengthen and regulate the cellular energy fields and body functions
- Enhance intercellular communication lending harmony to the integrated working of the various body systems and mechanisms
- Spark cellular energy
- Aid the body's innate power to drain toxins and flush out infective organisms
- Optimise exchange of oxygen, nutrients and body's natural chemicals.
- Enhance the function of the immune system, the self-repairing/renewing powers of the body, the person and the quality of life.
- Are synergistically combined to accelerate results

Appendix E

Child and Adolescent Mental Health Service (CAMHS)
www.obmh.nhs.uk

Introduction

The CAMHS Teams aim to provide help for children, young people and their families who are having moderate to severe emotional, behaviourable, development, psychological or relationship difficulties.

We see young people between the ages of 0-18 who are referred by their GP, health visitor, school of hospital doctor to either the Primary Child and Adolescent Mental Health Service (PCAMHS) in Oxfordshire or CAMHS in Buckinghamshire.

What you can expect from your team

During your assessment you will be able to discuss your mental health and social needs. After your assessment, which may take more than one session, your assessor will discuss with you what help can be provided by our service or another service to best meet your needs. If the team can help you, a Care Co-ordinator will work with you to organise your care. This person can be a:

Psychiatrist Doctors with specialist training in child and adolescent mental health. The Consultant has overall medical responsibility.

Community Psychiatric Nurse (CPN) Nurses with specialist knowledge of mental health who work directly with children and young people.

Clinical Psychologist Psychologists who had had specialist training in psychological approaches to the treatment of mental health problems in children, young people and their families.

Occupational Therapist (OT) Therapists who use play and other activities to understand and help with feelings and worries.

Psychotherapist Psychotherapists who have had specialist training in psychoanalytical approaches to the treatment of mental health problems in children, young people and their families.

Art Therapist Art Therapy is a form of psychotherapy that uses art media as its primary mode of communication.

Support Worker People who work directly in supporting children and young people.

Administrator Admin staff are front line staff members supporting the children and young people along with the clinical team.

Social Worker Employed by Health and Local Authority to work in health. They have specialist training in child development, family relationships, safe guarding children and child welfare issues.

Individual Therapist Therapists who work to help people use their own strengths to understand and change behaviour and feelings which can cause distress to themselves and their families.

Family Therapist Therapists who help families to make changes by working with all or parts of the family and listening to different perspectives of the same difficulties.

Appendix F

The Dove Clinic www.doveclinic.com

The approaches we use in life threatening illness do not have as good an evidence base as do conventional approaches, such as chemotherapy, radiotherapy, etc. The treatments we offer are by comparison, safer than conventional treatment modalities, but it is important to realise that significantly less research has been done with the approaches we offer than with conventional approaches. This is why our treatment programmes are offered on an 'informed consent' basis only. Therefore, it is important not to have false hopes as to what we might be able to achieve. We do not claim that any of our treatments, investigative procedures, or blood tests are cancer cures.

We have an academic approach to our work and have written several papers of a research nature to do with life threatening illnesses which are posted on our website.

We have formed a group of doctors in the UK who have an interest in treating life-threatening illness using the complementary integrated approach, at which we invite appropriate speakers to come and talk to us. Amongst these speakers are oncologists, particularly those who have a broadminded approach to the treatment of life threatening illness. These kinds of oncologists are increasing in numbers. We are also prepared to teach (by arrangement) individual doctors who have a special interest in the approaches we are using. We encourage research into the approaches used at The Dove Clinic for Integrated Medicine, and have a research charity called The Dove Healing Trust, which is set up to fund this kind of work. The reason for this is that conventional funding for these kind of studies tends not to be forthcoming.

We frequently work with oncologists and radiotherapists and we consistently find that a number of our approaches, especially organ-based complex homeopathy, based on the traditional Chinese model and methods for maintaining cell-mediated immunity, lead to much lower side effects from chemotherapy or radiotherapy. Specifically we find that hair loss and nausea occur less often with these approaches running concurrently with chemotherapy, and post-radiotherapy scarring is less common. We are planning to incorporate hyperthermia, a treatment that is known to enhance the effects of radiotherapy. Anti-oxidant therapy running alongside chemotherapy is a controversial area. A detailed discussion document on this issue by Frank Moss, comes down in favour of moderate anti-oxidant use during chemotherapy, even though chemotherapy is a pro-oxidant treatment.

The problem with life threatening illnesses is that they are complex illnesses and operate as systems rather than as linear processes in which cause A gives a result B. The science of genetic disorders giving rise to life threatening illnesses, is just such a complex process. This means therefore, that we would need a systems view of assessing these treatments in order to truly establish their value. This sort of research methodology does not exist currently; a research problem also for the majority of complementary medicine, which has a poor evidence base but an increasing number of patients – interestingly enough, doctors are major users! We are happy to answer questions from prospective patients: use the new customers form in the contact us section on our website: www.doveclinic.com We can recommend accommodation in London and in Hampshire, for patients when they stay for their intravenous infusion programmes.

If you have a tumour that is curable by surgery, or by any other conventional means, then we would most probably advise you to follow the conventional route, and we would provide supportive treatment approaches to reduce any damage which conventional approaches may have. If you chose to completely forego conventional treatment approaches with a conventional tumour, we would clearly have to state that in writing to you, and make sure that you know that the evidence base of the treatment we are offering is not as solid as that offered by conventional medicine.

Hockley Mill Stables
Church Lane
Twyford
Hampshire
SO21 1NT
Tel: 01962 718000
Fax: 01962 718011

Appendix G

The Issels Treatment Centre www.issels.com
www.cancershiddengifts.co.uk

The Issels Treatment is as integrative, non-toxic strategy for Cancer of all types and stages, always adjusted to the individual patient's needs and focused on the healing of the whole person.

The treatment programme consists of:

1. Specific Components, which are directed at the elimination of the Cancer cells and tumours.
2. Non-Specific Components, which normalise the internal bodily environment, the 'soil' on which the Cancer has grown, and restore the body's ability to fight the disease.

Non-specific Treatment:

The non-specific treatment is as important as the specific treatment. Over many years it has shown to be essential in optimising the effectiveness of the vaccines and other tumour-specific measures.

The treatment is designed to –

Remove causal factors

Repair damages to organs and organ systems

Restore regulatory and immune mechanisms

It attacks Cancer indirectly by eliminating the preconditions for its existence. It also helps prevent disease progression and recurrence.

The Issels strategy includes standard treatments if indicated. The Comprehensive Issels Treatment Programme has been shown to optimise the effectiveness and reduce the toxic side effects of standard treatments, such as radiation and chemotherapy.

The Non-Specific Treatment Components are non-toxic. They enhance each other by following a special treatment system developed over many years and include, but are not limited to, the following:

Nutritional immunotherapy primarily of organic foods (vegetables, freshly pressed vegetable juices, protein according to individual needs) is always adjusted to individual needs. It also includes

Intravenous nutrition and <u>nutraceuticals,</u> as well as anti-oxidants, minerals, trace elements, tissue salts, amino acids, herbal substances, as well as vitamins such as **Vitamin C**.

Co-Enzyme CO-Q10, is a powerful anti-oxidant. It has shown a strong anti-tumour effect in a breast Cancer trial in Copenhagen, Denmark. Principal investigator Karl Folkers reports regression of liver and lung tumours in a current German trial.

Melatonin.

Autohaemotherapy, a preparation from the patient's own blood, helps boost the immune system.

Enzymatic therapy improves digestion, the elimination of immune complexes and the break down of the fibrin coating of Cancer cells.

Oxidative therapies, such as:

Photoluminescence Therapy and **Ozone Therapy** improve cellular respiration and immunity.

Glandulars help regenerate organs such as the liver, the thyroid, the thymus gland and other glands.

Laetrile, also called Amygdalin or Vitamin B 17, has shown to attack Cancer without the toxic side effects of chemotherapy.

Polarising solution, which is a mixture of glucose, potassium, and insulin (GKI) administered intravenously has shown to reverse tissue damage (oedema) in normal tissue surrounding tumours, and to destabilise malignant growths by making them acid. This treatment was developed by Demetrio Sodi-Pallares, MD.

Phytotherapy with herbal medicinal products is administered according to individual requirements.

Urea/Creatine Therapy as part of our treatment program has shown over several years to be an important alternative method of tumour debulking in various types of Cancer. E.

Danopoulos published in respected journals many provocative reports of tumour responses to synthetic urea and creatine.

Reossification Therapy using substances such as calcitonin, clodronate, pamidronate, zolodronic acid, has shown to build-up Cancer-damaged bones.

Chelation Therapy

Detoxification procedures through improved function of the liver, kidneys, colon, lung and skin assist the body in its endeavours to get rid of metabolic waste and toxins that impair immune functions.

Colon Hydotherapy

Psychological Guidance and Emotional Support in single and group sessions enhance the effectiveness of all other treatment components.

Physical Therapy.

Rationale

Cancer patients' immune and regulatory mechanisms fail to recognise Cancer cells and eliminate them. They tolerate them.

The Issels comprehensive immunotherapy is designed to break through this 'tolerance'. It is a unique blend of non-toxic treatment modalities that complement and enhances one another in an effort to attack the Cancer and at the same time to restore the body's regulatory, repair and defence systems, of which the immune system is one important part. In general terms, some of these treatments work on the levels of the biochemical defence and help Cancer cells undergo differentiation as encoded in the genes that cause them to die through programmed cell death called apoptosis. Other treatment modalities work on the levels of cell-mediated and humoral immunities. It is a proprietary program that is only available at the Issels Treatment Centres. The Issels Treatment strategy includes standard treatments when indicated.

Appendix G1 –

Vaccines

1. Coley's Mixed Bacterial Vaccine

Issels website: 'This vaccine activates the innate immune system. It opens blockades in the body's connective tissues, enhances the formation of the body's own interferons, interleukins, colony stimulating factors, tumour necrosis factor, and other potent disease fighters'

2. Dendritic Cell Vaccine

(Extracorporeal photopheresis with the autologous dendritic cell vaccine)

Issels website: 'This painless procedure works in the following way: Via the Photopheresis device, pathogens and abnormal cells are destroyed through exposure to ultraviolet light, which also has an enormous immune-boosting effect. During this procedure, monocytes are separated from the blood then cultured to maturity; converting them to active Dendritic cells. These are injected into the patient in small customized doses over several months. Dendritic cells are responsible for identifying pathogens (viruses, fungi, bacteria) and malignant cells, by presenting their identifying markers (antigens) to specific T lymphocytes, which then multiply and attack only the identified diseased cells, not normal healthy cells'.

3. Issels Autologous Vaccine

Issels Website: 'This vaccine works in a very complex way to enhance the immune functions. It is prepared from the patient's own blood, which represents his/her own unique internal environment. The preparation follows procedures that favor the development of antigenic peptides and other immunogenic compounds in the fight against Cancer and other immune disorders. Experience has shown that it stimulates formation and activation of macrophages, T-helper cells, and natural killer cells'.

My Personal Issels Programme

Room for patient and companion for 28 days and nights.

Three meals a day for the companion.

Daily visits by the medical staff.
Nursing attendance 24 hours a day.
Admission physical exam and discharge physical exam.
Electrocardiogram.
Chest X-rays as indicated and CT-scan.
Labs (Wellness Profile 71-CBC, Chemzyme plus, Urinalysis, Thyroid Panel, PT, PTT activated).
Tumour markers
HCV RNA V PCR, QT. HIV test.
Dark field blood examination.
Double Lumen Catheter. 2 cuvettes.
Nutritional immunotherapy (including vitamins, minerals, enzymes, nutraceuticals, glandulars, tissue salts, phytochemicals, detoxification, Enzyme therapy.
Blood oxygenation.
Intravenous vitamin C therapy.
Polarizing solutions (glucose/insulin/potassium.
Kemdalin as indicated.
Urea/creatine therapy.
Colonics.
Physical therapy.
Extracorporeal Photopheresis.
Culture of Dendritic Cell Vaccine.
Administrations of Dendritic Cell Vaccine depending on patient's response and home supply for several months depending on the yield of the culture.
Coley's vaccine, supply for 6 months.
Autologous Issels Vaccine, supply for 6 months.
Photoluminescence treatments

Appendix H

Project Oasis of Hope is a volunteer ministry that is within Oasis of Hope Hospital in the Issels Treatment Centre in Playas de Tijuana, Mexico. Our goal is to offer daily encouragement, times of prayer and companionship during a difficult time in the lives of the patient and the companion and to encourage hope and to offer eternal life through Jesus Christ our Lord.

Project Oasis of Hope was founded by Kleon and Kathy Cronk when they came to Oasis Hospital as companions for Bruce and Vicky Northey. Bruce was eventually cured of a cancerous tumour. During their stay, both couples found themselves involved in ministry among the patients and companions. After much prayer and planning, Project Oasis of Hope was born.

This ministry began a year later in January of 1989, and has continued with great success. Many people have been led to the Lord with spiritual comfort and miraculous healing along the way.

Project Oasis of Hope is always looking for individuals who are mission-minded to volunteer to serve for a period of one to two months. The volunteers are known as 'Armigos de Esperanza', which means 'Friends of Hope'.

'Now may the God of hope fill you with all joy and peace in believing, that you may abound in hope by the power of the Holy Spirit'. Romans 15:13 NKJ

We desire your prayer support in this ministry and if you would like to partner with Project Oasis of Hope, please contact us below.

Project Oasis of Hope is a 503c3 non-profit ministry. You will receive a tax deductible receipt when cheques are made out to Project Oasis of Hope or when using PayPal on our websites.

Project Oasis of Hope
PO Box 435298, San Ysidro CA 92143, USA
www.projectoasisofhope.org
Email: vbamigos@yahoo.com
001 (619) 518-2366
www.sharinghopenow.com – sign up for newsletters

Appendix I

Sequence of Appointments with Health Professionals encountered along the way including: breast nurses, general consultants, breast cancer consultants, registrars, GPs, district nurses, junior doctors, nurses, ward sisters, tea ladies, shop staff, radiologists, reception staff, anaesthetists, other patients.

2004

7 April	Visit to GP for hormone replacement therapy
20 April	Hospital for mammogram
26 April	Consultant at hospital for results of mammogram
12 May	Hospital for biopsy
26 May	Consultant at hospital for results of biopsy
30 May	Breast cancer consultant at hospital
1 June	Hospital for pre-op assessment
10 June	Hospital for first surgery – lumpectomy
16 June	District nurse's visit to remove stitches
25 June	Breast cancer consultant at hospital for results
8 July	Hospital for second surgery – wider local excision
14 July	District nurse's home visit to remove stitches
18 July	Consultant at hospital for results
3 Aug	Pre-op assessment
5 Aug	Hospital for third surgery – wider local excision
12 Aug	District nurse's visit to remove stitches
23 Aug	Breast cancer consultant for results
7 Sept	GP
9 Sept	Hospital to see consultant
	Hospice to attend advisory clinic
16 Sept	Hospital for fourth surgery – mastectomy
22 Sept	District Nurse's visit to remove stitches
4 Oct	Consultant at hospital for mastectomy results
11 Oct	Breast cancer consultant at hospital
18 Oct	Breast cancer consultant at hospital
5 Nov	Hospital – prosthesis fitting
9 Nov	Oncologist at hospital for follow on treatment
1 Dec	Amoena in Southampton for mastectomy lingerie

7 Dec	Oncologist again and visit to lymphatic drainage advisor

2005

5 Mar	Dr. Rosy Daniel of Health Creation in Bristol
25 April	6-month check with breast cancer consultant
10 May	Further surgery to remove cyst along scar line
23 May	Consultant at hospital for results
14 June	Oncologist at hospital
27 June	Dr. Simi Khanna – wholistic doctor in Aylesbury
19 July	Cancer oncologist at different hospital for second opinion
3 Aug	Pre-Planning meeting at hospital for radiotherapy
12 Aug	Hospital for radiotherapy
31 Aug	Family Support Centre (CAMHS)
5 Sept	Radiotherapy
7 Sept	Radiotherapy
9 Sept	Radiotherapy
12 Sept	GP for blood test
	Art therapy at CAMHS
13 Sept	Radiotherapy
15 Sept	Radiotherapy
19 Sept	Radiotherapy
	Art therapy at CAMHS
21 Sept	Radiotherapy
23 Sept	Visit to oncologist
27 Sept	Radiotherapy
	Art therapy at CAMHS
29 Sept	Radiotherapy
3 Oct	Radiotherapy
5 Oct	Radiotherapy
	Art therapy at CAMHS
7 Oct	Radiotherapy
18 Nov	Oncologist : HER2 test
	Art therapy at CAMHS
23 Dec	Oncologist: HER2 test results

2006

25 Jan	Hospital for CT scan

9 Feb	Oncologist for results
2 Mar	Hospital for first intravenous dose of Herceptin
24 March	Herceptin
13 April	GP – first Zoladex injection
18 April	Hospital for CT scan
21 April	Herceptin and appointment with Oncologist
10 May	Dr. Simi Khanna – infusions of ozone, minerals
11 May	GP for Zoladex injection
12 May	Oncologist Herceptin
15 May	Dr. Simi Khanna for infusions
16 May	Hospital for echo heart scan
25 May	Dr. Simi Khanna
2 June	Herceptin
7 June	GP – Zoladex
20 June	Oncologist
23 June	Herceptin
5 July	Hospital for CT Scan
10 July	CAMHS
14 July	Oncologist for scan results
1 August	GP re: Zoladex
4 August	Herceptin
	Prosthesis fitting
10 August	Dr. Simi Khanna
15 August	Hospital for echo heart scan
24 August	GP – Zoladex
25 August	Herceptin
8 Sept	CAMHS Josh and myself
15 Sept	Herceptin
21 Sept	GP – Zoladex
22 Sept	Dr. Simi Khanna
6 Oct	Herceptin
19 Oct	GP – Zoladex
27 Oct	Herceptin
20 Nov	Herceptin
8 Dec	Herceptin
29 Dec	Herceptin

2007

15 Jan	Dr. Julian Kenyon of The Dove Clinic
19 Jan	Herceptin
23 Jan	Oncologist
26 Jan	GP – Zoladex
9 Feb	Hospital for CT Scan
	CAMHS
16 Feb	Echo heart scan
20 Feb	Issels Immunotherapy Clinic
21 Feb	Issels
22 Feb	Issels
23 Feb	Issels
24 Feb	Issels
25 Feb	Issels
26 Feb	Issels
27 Feb	Issels
28 Feb	Issels
1 Mar	Issels
2 Mar	Issels
3 Mar	Issels
4 Mar	Issels
5 Mar	Issels
6 Mar	Issels
7 Mar	Issels
8 Mar	Issels
9 Mar	Issels
10 Mar	Issels
11 Mar	Issels
12 Mar	Issels
13 Mar	Issels
14 Mar	Issels
15 Mar	Issels
16 Mar	Issels
17 Mar	Issels
18 Mar	Issels
19 Mar	Issels
20 Mar	Issels

22 Mar	GP for Zoladex
1 April	Starting the Issels vaccines at home
13 April	Oncologist at hospital
17 April	Restart Herceptin
26 April	GP – Zoladex
28 April	Injecting myself at home!
8 May	Herceptin
29 May	Herceptin
6 June	GP – Zoladex
8 June	Oncologist
19 June	Herceptin
10 July	Herceptin
31 July	Herceptin
21 Aug	Herceptin
24 Aug	Oncologist
11 Sept	Herceptin
2 Oct	Herceptin
23 Oct	Herceptin
13 Nov	Herceptin
4 Dec	Herceptin
31 Dec	Herceptin

2008

22 Jan	Herceptin
14 Feb	Herceptin
22 Feb	CT scan
6 Mar	Herceptin
8 May	Herceptin
19 June	Herceptin
10 July	Herceptin
31 July	Herceptin
15 Aug	Oncologist
18 Aug	Echo
21 Aug	Herceptin
11 Sept	Herceptin

... and continuing

Helpful Websites

www. issels.com
www.cancershiddengifts.co.uk
www.globalretreatcentre.org
www.obmh.nhs.uk
www.healthcreation.co.uk
www.doveclinic.com
www.allpeoplephotography.com
www.aylesburyspace.co.uk

Book References and Suggested Reading

When Things Fall Apart by Pema Chodron
Touching Peace by Thich Nhat Hanh
You Can Heal Your Life by Louise L.Hay
The Tibetan Book of Living and Dying by Sogyal Rinpoche
The Shack by William P. Young
Living In The Light by Shakti Gawain
New Habits:Today's Women Who Choose to Become
Nuns by Isabel Losada
Travelling Light by Max Lucado
A Visible Wound' by Julie Friedeberger.
Cancer: A Second Opinion by Josef Issels 1999
Holy Bible